To the Markets of the World

Colorado Shale Deposits

Offshore geophysical exploration

Wilmington Refinery

BAKERSFIELD

N

SANTA PAULA

NEWHALL

VENTURA

LOS ANGELES

SAN BERNARDINO

BREA 76

Outer Harbor Developement at Los Angeles

First Geological Department

First Commercial Dry Ice From Petroleum

Fuel for our

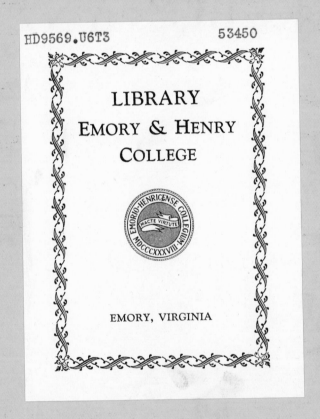

# BLACK BONANZA

FRANK J. TAYLOR is the co-author of OH, RANGER!, DEMOCRACY'S AIR ARSENAL, and other books and has contributed many articles to *The Saturday Evening Post, Country Gentleman, Holiday,* and *The Reader's Digest.* EARL M. WELTY is a former editor of daily newspapers in California and Hawaii and a contributor to *Collier's, Harper's* and other national magazines.

# BLACK
# BONANZA

*How an Oil Hunt Grew*

*into the Union Oil Company of California*

## FRANK J. TAYLOR
### AND
## EARL M. WELTY

WHITTLESEY HOUSE

McGRAW-HILL BOOK COMPANY, INC.   NEW YORK. LONDON. TORONTO

# Black Bonanza

Published by the McGraw-Hill Book Company, Inc.
Printed in the United States of America

# Contents

*CHAPTER ONE*

# Black Bonanza

NO Machine Age miracle has changed the lives of Americans more than the Black Bonanza, which dates from 1855, a year in which a quarter of a million eager prospectors were frantically overturning the Sierra Nevada foothills for their share of California's fabulous Gold Bonanza, which then seemed far more fabulous than petroleum. While Yankees sweated and fought for the precious yellow metal, two Mexican prospectors, General Andreas Pico and his nephew Romulo, were digging pits unnoticed in a canyon north of San Fernando Mission in Southern California. From these pits the Picos scooped up a black, sticky tar which they sold at the mission for healing and illuminating uses. The Picos were completely unaware that they were pioneering an industry destined to change the tempo, the living, the shape, and the size of the world.

One exceptional Forty-niner who may have sensed the importance of the Picos' oil strike was a New York sperm-oil dealer, George S. Gilbert. While others scrambled for gold, Gilbert was busily devising a crude refinery near Ventura Mission to boil off the vapors of black petroleum from pits in Sulphur Mountain, at the lower end of the same valley in which the Picos mined tar. Gilbert sold the heavy residue of his still as a grease for squeaky ox-cart axles, and in 1857 he consigned a hundred kegs of his rock oil to A. C. Ferris of Brooklyn, New York. Unfortunately, transporting the kegs of oil across the Isthmus of Panama by muleback proved so difficult that the muleteers dumped the consignment in the jungle.

Had Gilbert's oil reached the New York market on schedule, the monument marking the birthplace of the oil industry might well have been on San Antonio Creek in Southern California instead of at Titusville on Oil Creek in Pennsylvania, where Uncle Billy Smith, the blacksmith, punched the hole in the earth that was to be this country's first oil well. That year, 1857, oil was first found at Ploesti, Ru-

1

*Highly productive Santa Fe Springs field discovered in 1921 by Union Oil shows how the petroleum industry conserves resources through orderly development. A field crowded with poorly spaced and unnecessary wells would be wasteful.*

mania. At Pittsburgh Sam Kier, the druggist, was bottling crude petroleum as "rock oil, celebrated for its wonderful curative powers." Then came the eventful year 1859, when the Drake well touched off the Pennsylvania oil stampede, a scramble as wild in its way as was the California Gold Rush.

The men who pioneered the petroleum industry, both in California and in Pennsylvania, wanted crude oil for purposes that seem ridiculous today. "Colonel" Edwin L. Drake and his backers and their oil-mad rivals thought of a barrel of crude oil only as rock oil which could be used "both internally and externally" and for a cheaper source of so-called "coal oil." At the time, illuminating oil was extracted either from whales or from coal, both expensive processes. General Pico likewise was motivated by the belief that "fossil oil" would cure man's aches and light his nights. Gilbert hit on the bigger idea of lubricants; to get them, he had to boil off the volatile gases, thus percolating into the thin air the most efficient package of power that man would find until the Atomic Age dawned a century later.

The Black Bonanza was overshadowed by the more spectacular California Gold

2

*Hundreds of refineries supply America's 34,000 competing companies. This huge Los Angeles plant of Union Oil processes 60,000 barrels a day. Its 300 steel tanks hold 5,895,007 barrels of both crude and refined petroleum.*

Rush. Men wanted gold because it was the token of wealth. In time the gold they wrested from California's hills and rivers, roughly 3 billion dollars' worth, found its way back underground in vaults at Fort Knox, Kentucky, and Denver, Colorado. The oil from beneath California's soils exceeded even the wildest predictions of Professor Benjamin Silliman, Jr., of Yale, that it would aggregate "more than all the whales in the Pacific Ocean" could yield. By 1950 the yearly yield of California oil wells alone approached in dollar value the output of all the state's gold mines since gold's discovery.

None of the pioneers of the original Black Bonanza, nor their contemporaries who punched holes for oil in Ohio, West Virginia, New York, and neighboring states, had the slightest notion of what was in a barrel of oil. No early prospector or producer dreamed that each barrel of petroleum flowing out of the earth contained the makings of over four thousand potential products which, within the next century, would change the living of civilized peoples.

Among the pioneers of Pennsylvania's Oil Creek petroleum boom was one who later helped found California's oil indus-

3

Costly, gigantic equipment, such as this five-ton block, swivel and elevators, is needed to drill wells nearly four miles beneath surface.

try and who lived to see petroleum become the lifeblood of the mechanized rubber-tired modern world. He was Lyman Stewart of Titusville, Pennsylvania, Santa Paula and Los Angeles, California, one of the few key characters in the fabulous story of oil whose life and works bridge the years from the muddy, brawling days of Pennsylvania's oil rush to the pipelined petroleum business that is today one of the country's key industries.

Nine short decades after the discovery of oil, it is hard to imagine the havoc that would result if all of the country's oil wells were, by some catastrophic miracle, to go dry tomorrow. Imagine a world without oil. Think of highways without automobiles. Or modern industry without trucks. Agriculture without tractors. Railroads without diesels or oil-burning loco-

Most of America's oil wells must be expensively pumped to get out the petroleum. This huge pump operated at Union Oil's Playa Del Rey field has a 10-foot stroke compared with the average of only three or four feet.

4

*About 1¼ million oil wells have been drilled in America—and one out of every four has been a "duster." An average well costs around $50,000. Crew above is lowering sharp new bit through rotary table which later will revolve 200 times a minute to keep bit cutting.*

*Some wells produce salt as well as oil. These spherical dehydrators automatically desalt 1,500 barrels an hour by mixing heated crude and fresh water, then removing the salt solution. Salt-free oil may then be sent directly to pipelines. In foreground is a well being pumped.*

motives. Travel without planes. Homes heated without oil or natural gas. Control of insects and weed pests without petroleum chemicals. Roads without asphalt. Life without a host of everyday products —plastics, solvents, paints, tires, detergents, cosmetics, inks—synthesized in whole or in part from the onetime residue in a barrel of oil. Or free peoples defending themselves from the dictatorships without the military striking power of the man-made global rivers of oil that turned the tide of victory in World War II.

As a demonstration of what rugged individualism and free enterprise under controls, some voluntary and others imposed by states and federal governments, can achieve to better the lot of mankind, the oil industry is a striking example. Oil in its first century has had chalked against it nearly all of the mistakes that it is possible for one industry to make. It has weathered the century's most vicious ef-

6

*America's petroleum industry works around the clock as it turns out some 4,000 different products. This towering 268-foot TCC Unit (Thermofor Catalytic Cracking) produces high-octane gasoline at the Los Angeles refinery of Union Oil.*

fort at monopoly and emerged as an industry of 34,000 competitors fiercely fighting for the consumer's dollar. The oil industry has wasted untold billions of horsepower of energy that can never be whistled back out of the air. It has survived price wars, gouging, squeezes, grasping production methods, arrogant displays of wealth.

On the credit side, its workers have been better paid than those of any other wage group in the world. It has offered its consumers more choice of better products and more services than any other industry. Its oil hunters have scoured the globe to increase the backlog of this gift of the ages to modern generations. The proven reserves of this stored-up treasure of time, the fossil energy conserved in petroleum, have increased prodigiously. And oil scientists have never let up in their feverish search for more products from the barrel of oil.

As Reese H. Taylor, president of Union Oil Company, says, "We have just started

7

*World's greatest oil reservoir is the stadium-shaped structure at upper left which holds 4,000,000 barrels. With the 24 steel tanks holding another 2,340,000 barrels, Union Oil's Torrance Tank Farm has a capacity of 6,340,000 barrels.*

to unlock the secrets in a barrel of oil." Other industry heads agree with him that there are almost innumerable combinations in the petroleum hydrocarbon chain, once its links are broken down.

The industry has grown so fantastically that it is next to impossible for even oil men to understand how it all came about. Oil runs into astronomical figures. To supply the United States alone calls for 5.75 million barrels a day, or 242 million gallons of oil products each twenty-four hours. That means over 2 billion barrels a year, which is to say, 89 billion gallons. To supply this demand, the oil industry has drilled 450,000 wells and employed nearly 2 million Americans. Oil products

produced in this country sell for more than 10 billion dollars every year.

This river of oil flows from proven underground reserves aggregating 76 billion barrels. To find and develop this oil river, Americans have invested 23 billion dollars in wells, pipelines, refineries, distribution systems, and service stations. The industry spends 100 million dollars a year in research, one-seventh of the total spent by all United States industry for that purpose. Yet despite the prodigious outlay, oil scientists have barely unlocked the secrets of a barrel of oil.

The easier way to comprehend the impact of this sprawling behemoth industry, which reaches into every community and nearly every home, is to take one oil company and see how one thing led to another, until it became a sizable giant in its own right. Union Oil Company of California is a fair cross section of the industry as a whole. Union is unique in that because of the pioneering of one of its founders, Lyman Stewart, in Pennsylvania, it bridges the complete life span of the oil business. Third-generation Stewarts are still key figures in Union, although

Union is no longer a family company. One advantage to telling the oil story through Union's experiences is that the records of the company, going back to the beginning, are intact and available. Another is that Union, although one of the "Big Twenty," is still classified as an independent. There are a dozen oil companies in the country larger than Union, but Union has grown big and lusty by fighting the battles of the small independ-

*Modern refinery units such as this Thermal Cracker at the Oleum Refinery of Union Oil Company are a veritable maze of pipes, stills, valves and gadgets costing upwards of many millions of dollars to squeeze more and better products from a barrel of petroleum.*

ent producers and distributors. Union has grubstaked thousands of Americans in their own businesses.

Finally, Union's imposing list of "firsts" justifies the choice of this colorful enter-priser as an example of how the prodigious oil industry blossomed to maturity. Union built the first tanker on the Pacific Coast; it laid the first pipeline from the oil fields to tidewater; it first spanned the Isthmus of Panama with a pipeline from the Pacific to the Atlantic; its shopmen perfected the first oil burner and converted the first Western locomotive to oil; its drillers punched the first deep wells; they first cemented wells to shut out water; they also brought in the West's first and the world's largest gushers. Union established the first oil geology department and built the first petroleum laboratory on the Pacific Coast. The company's refiners made the first printers' ink from California petroleum. They first found the way to separate asphalt and waxes from Western crude oil, and made the first lubricating oils from California oils. They produced the first highway asphalt from petroleum. The company pioneered underground storage of gas. It was first to use the gas-lift method for getting oil out of the ground. Its drillers developed the deep-well tools that tapped lower basins. Union's scientists, hunting ways of extracting more treasures from a barrel of oil, perfected the unique hypersorption process for separating the chemical components of petroleum gases. They devised a revolutionary new method of extracting oil from shales.

From a little wildcatting operation at Santa Paula and Newhall, Union grew, like the United States oil industry as a whole, until its oil hunters probed the earth from Alaska to Paraguay, and even the continental shelf under the Gulf of Mexico and the Pacific Ocean, for more oil to yield more products for a million customers in eleven states and two territories. The company withstood half-a-dozen efforts of larger oil companies to swallow it, and emerged as the champion of the independent producers for whom it provided a dependable market.

These and a dozen other pioneering "firsts" are all a part of the Union story, a saga of how men of courage and vision built the flourishing industry that furnishes the lifeblood of modern living. This, then, is the story of Union's role in the Black Bonanza.

# CHAPTER TWO

# Birth of an Age

WITHOUT Lyman Stewart there would have been no Union Oil Company of California. Hence any account of Union's role in the Black Bonanza must start from the village of Cherrytree on Oil Creek in northwestern Pennsylvania, where Lyman Stewart was born on July 22, 1840.

Stewart was already a veteran oil operator when he reached California's drowsing petroleum fields late in 1882. "Born to oil" only 10 miles from Titusville, where the world's first oil well was drilled in 1859, he had plunged in oil ventures several times, had made and lost one fortune, and had partially recouped by the time he reached California. From the tree-clad hills of northwest Pennsylvania, he brought to the rugged, undeveloped West the foresight, the faith, and the hard-won experience needed to spearhead a spectacular social, economic, and spiritual revolution throughout the Pacific area. By this time, Lyman Stewart was forty-two years old, the head of a family; he had

fought through three years of Civil War, had invented drilling tools, and devised new oil production methods. He had pioneered petroleum conservation and had struggled against wasteful overproduction. He had played an active role in the hectic pioneering days of the Pennsylvania oil boom.

Young Lyman was nineteen when oil fever swept the Venango Valley in which the Stewarts, thrifty Scotch stock, had lived since 1802. Lyman's forebears squandered no time at the neighborhood pastime of collecting oil from the creeks and pits of the surrounding area. His father, William, was one of the valley's two tanners. Lyman, the second of several children, was chosen to carry on the family tanning business, which he hated. Nevertheless, the youngster began as an apprentice at eleven to learn the trade among the stinking vats and hides. One of his chores was to tramp and ride the wooded hills and lowlands to pick up hides from farmers and deliver leather to

11

*Lyman Stewart was nineteen when he lost his entire fortune of $125 investing in oil.*

them, a task that stood him well when the oil boom broke, because he had learned every foot of the valley firsthand. He knew the rivulets and the oil seeps, a knowledge that gave him a decided advantage later in buying and selling oil leases.

The Stewarts were recognized as a quietly substantial family, not poor but certainly not rich. The family's ties were exceptionally strong. So was each member's close and sincere adherence to the Presbyterian faith. Every evening Lyman's mother, who was an Irwin, another Scotch strain, read the Bible aloud to the seven

children. At the close of the reading period, family prayers ended the day and candles were snuffed out. William Stewart worked hard at his trade and labored equally diligently for his church, helping to raise funds for the first Presbyterian church to be erected in the Titusville area. He occasionally preached in this simple frame structure when bad weather delayed the circuit-riding pastor. Each of the children was confirmed here. This close tie with church affairs, begun so early in Lyman Stewart's life, inspired him in later years to dedicate much of his fortune to building churches, educating pastors, and otherwise aiding the spread of Christianity.

The village of Cherrytree, at the time of Lyman Stewart's birth, consisted of four families, with a dozen other homes scattered among the wooded hills. The school was primitive, even for those days. The next larger one was 10 miles away at Titusville, so Lyman and his brothers and sisters went to the tiny one-room school close to home. The last of Lyman's five grades of formal school learning was spent at Titusville, which at that time had little excitement to offer. It was more a village than a town, spread out on the floor of a broad valley. The community boasted a population of nearly four hundred persons, a count that often doubled or trebled on Saturday night when the loggers came to town. Though the nearest railroad ended at Corry, 27 miles to the north via a rutty, muddy, nearly impassable road, Titusville was the trading center for the surrounding lumbering and farming area. There were three churches,

Presbyterian, Universalist, and Methodist, and two taverns in the center of town. Most of Titusville's citizens were of good, sound pioneer stock, sufficient unto themselves.

Though the schools, both at Titusville and Cherrytree, were unpretentious, Lyman Stewart sat with several classmates whose names were to go down in history along with his own. One was John W. Steele, later to become a legendary character known as "Coal Oil Johnny," when, inheriting a fortune of $200,000 and a daily income of $2,000, he rollicked off to New York and began an orgy of spending that classed him with Diamond Jim Brady and ended when the wells ran dry

and he returned to Titusville to spend the rest of his life wrestling baggage. Another was D. G. Scofield, who, like Stewart, learned the oil game in Pennsylvania and then migrated to California to head the business that later became the Standard Oil Company of California and Stewart's lustiest rival for oil and for markets.

Everybody in the neighborhood knew there was oil in the Venango Valley. It seeped out of the soil in rivulets and polluted Oil Creek, which flowed through the valley to the Allegheny River and on down to Pittsburgh. It gathered in hundreds of pits that were regarded as relics of either Indian or French diggings. A map of Pennsylvania, drawn in 1755, had

*Lady Stewart Well in Shamburg, Pennsylvania, was partially owned by Lyman Stewart. Its dividends helped pay family bills in California when finances were at lowest ebb. Well believed to have been named for Mrs. Jane Irwin Stewart, mother of Lyman.*

*Samuel M. Kier, a Pennsylvania salt merchant, sold bottled petroleum as medicine.*

the name "Petroleum" on it close to what was later to become Titusville, capital of the oil industry. During the Revolutionary War, General Benjamin Lincoln, whose weary troops passed through the valley and paused to bathe their feet and joints in the oil floating on the surface of the creek, reported:

"In the northern parts of Pennsylvania there is a creek called Oil Creek which empties itself into the Allegheny River, issuing from a spring on top of which floats an oil similar to what is called 'Barbados tar' and from which may be collected several gallons a day. The troops in marching that way halted at the spring,

collecting the oil and bathing their joints in it. This gave them great relief and freed them immediately from the rheumatic complaints with which many of them were afflicted."

The petroleum which seeped from the ground was also known as "Seneca oil" because the Seneca Indians collected it to barter with other tribes. Timothy Alden, first president of Allegheny College, Meadville, Pennsylvania, was probably the first to suggest the commercial possibilities of petroleum. He wrote in 1820:

"In the flats of Oil Creek, 28 miles southeasterly from Meadville, many oblong pits have been dug several feet deep, in the bottom of which Seneca oil, or petroleum, oozes and floats to the surface of the water. Whether the pits are the work of the French, who in the former part of the last century had military establishments on our principal streams, or of that people of whom no traditions have reached our time, but of whose judgment and skill in the arts of fortifying there are numerous evidences, it is impossible to resolve. By extending this operation, this oil called by the Senecas 'au nus' might be collected so as to become a profitable article of commerce. Fifteen barrels were once taken in one season from a single pit. It was formerly sold at $2 a gallon. The common price is now $1.50. It is one of the most penetrating liquids in nature. No wooden or oaken vessel is impervious to this; even a glass in which it has stood for some time cannot be cleared of the scent of it. This oil is much esteemed for its efficacy in removing rheumatic complaints. It burns well in lamps, and might be advantageously used in lighting streets. If by some process it could be rendered inodorous, it would become an important article for domestic illumination."

The first man to make real money out of the petroleum that seeped from the soil was Samuel Kier, a Pittsburgh druggist. Kier collected the petroleum that floated to the surface with the brine from a salt well operated by his father at Tarentum, on the Allegheny River about 50 miles south of Titusville. This he marketed in bottles for medicinal purposes, calling it "Kier's Rock Oil." It was lauded as a cure-all to be used both internally and externally. Another by-product was known as "Kier's Petroleum Butter." This was a greasy substance that gathered on the iron parts of the pump with each stroke of the sucker rod. Kier put it up in little boxes and sold it for burns, scalds, and bruises, and did a thriving business with the gold miners of the West, who "were always banging themselves up."

One day a youngster tossed a blazing torch into a canal on which a quantity of oil was floating, and the whole canal for a distance of half a mile or so burst into flames. This demonstrated to Kier that the greasy stuff, a nuisance not only in the salt works but also to canal-boat operators, would undoubtedly burn and that it would make both light and heat. Kier undertook to refine the oil and sell it as an illuminant. He did so fairly successfully in Pittsburgh, but was unable to mar-

*Prof. Benjamin Silliman, Jr., of Yale wrote glowing report of rivers of oil in the West.*

ket it very extensively in competition with coal oil, which was extracted by distilling coal, and with sperm oil which the whalers brought in from the sea. These and candles were the principal illuminants of the period.

The man who transformed the life of the peaceful Venango Valley—and that of Lyman Stewart as well—was no Pennsylvanian at all, but a Connecticut train conductor, Edwin L. Drake. Though Drake is hailed as the "Father of the Oil Industry," his role was something of a lucky accident, as a recheck of history shows.

About 1853, Francis Beattie Brewer, a doctor of Titusville, took a small bottle of Oil Creek petroleum with him when

15

he visited Dartmouth College, where he asked the Chemistry Department to analyze it. The college chemists reported the sample to be oil of apparent value, but made no recommendation for its use. A few weeks later George H. Bissell, a businessman of New Haven, Connecticut, saw the sample and the report while visiting Dartmouth. He became so interested that he journeyed to Titusville with J. G. Eveleth, his partner. Together they acquired from Brewer-Watson & Company what was considered the most promising oil land in Pennsylvania, 100 acres in fee simple and 112 acres on lease, paying $5,000 in cash. The land was about 2½ miles north of Titusville.

Returning to New Haven, Bissell and Eveleth organized the Pennsylvania Rock Oil Company, the first petroleum company in the United States. The company recovered oil from the seepages and sold it for $1.50 a gallon. In 1855 they hired Professor Benjamin A. Silliman, Jr., of Yale, to analyze their oil and find more extensive uses for it. Professor Silliman concluded that a useful kerosene or synthetic coal oil, and a number of other products, could be refined from the crude petroleum. It was the professor's report that drew the curtain on the dawn of the oil age.

Some of the stockholders of the Pennsylvania Rock Oil Company objected to spending real money on the oil gamble. So a new company, the Seneca Oil Company, was organized by Bissell and Eveleth, with the help of James M. Townsend, president of the City Savings Bank of New Haven. The Seneca Oil Company

took over the Bissell-Eveleth property near Titusville, and the directors looked around for someone to put down a well, similar to those being drilled in the area for salt water. Townsend picked Edwin L. Drake, a retired railroad conductor, largely because Drake was able to get a free pass on the Pennsylvania Railroad to go out and investigate the company's oil property. Townsend, being a canny promoter, also tagged Drake with the title of "Colonel." Thereafter he was always known as "Colonel Drake."

Though the "Colonel" knew nothing about oil, he was a man of action. Arriving at Corry, he rode horseback to Titusville, inspected the property, decided where a well should be drilled, and scouted the neighborhood for a driller. His quest brought him in contact with "Uncle Billy" Smith, a blacksmith and toolmaker, whom he hired. While Uncle Billy pounded a hole into the ground to bring in oil by the barrel, he and Drake became the laughingstock of the people of the valley. The operation was known, of course, as "Drake's Folly." The name stuck until August 20, 1859, when the hole was down 69½ feet. On Sunday morning Uncle Billy peered down into the stovepipe casing, an original idea devised by Drake to keep the well from caving in, and saw a black substance only a few feet from the surface.

Drake had struck oil. Despite all the ridicule, he had struck it by drilling for it. It was the first time in history that oil had been produced in that manner. The oil industry was born that day among the trees lining the banks of Oil Creek. The cry of "Oil! Oil!" spread like wildfire through the valley, and the peaceful scene was soon broken by one of the maddest, wildest land stampedes in history. Everyone scrambled to lease ground upon which to drill an oil well. Oil was selling at the time at $20 a barrel at the well site. Everyone in the valley decided to get rich overnight.

As Monday dawned, the influx of oil-mad outsiders began. Before the day was over, hundreds of strangers had poured into Titusville, and thousands more were on their way. Wildly excited, they milled about, buying, leasing, selling land with such enthusiasm that shortly every acre of the valley and even land far back in the hills had been leased. No one figured at the time that there was oil under the hills, but land was land and few questions were asked by the eager oil-lease hunters.

This get-rich-quick excitement failed to arouse Lyman Stewart unduly. He heard the thrilling news as he stepped from the church at Cherrytree, where the Stewart family made up a good part of the congregation. Young Lyman was nineteen at the time. He had completed his apprenticeship as a tanner and was entitled to practice the trade as a journeyman. Hating it as much as ever, he considered offering himself as a missionary. A wave of evangelism was sweeping the country, and the churches were calling for self-sacrificing volunteers to spread the gospel among the heathen. Lyman Stewart had saved up $125, a lot of money in 1859 for a young fellow not yet of age.

But by December the oil fever, plus the possession of so much cash capital,

"Colonel" Edwin L. Drake (right) with his friend Peter Wilson at America's first oil well.

had changed his mind about becoming a missionary—a decision that, paradoxically, would enable him later to endow churches and Bible schools on a magnificent scale. He invested his $125 in a one-eighth interest in a lease on the John Benninghoff farm. It took all of his capital; and unfortunately his partners were strapped, too, by the time they had planked down the $1,000 demanded by the cagey old German for the right to drill on his land. The young promoters had no resources with which to finance drilling a well. They lost the lease and their savings. Six years later, in 1865, when others drilled on the Benninghoff farm, the first hole was a 300-barrels-per-day well. Shrewd old John Benninghoff cut up his farm into small lots and leased them at

17

peak boom prices. Within a short time, he had an income of $6,000 a day. Distrusting banks, he kept his royalties in an old safe in the front room of his house. One day four robbers entered the home, lined up the family, broke open the strongbox, and carried away $200,000 in one of the most sensational robberies of the area and of the day. Thus, in his first plunge in oil, a fortune slipped through Lyman Stewart's fingers. It was merely the first Lyman Stewart was to lose in his jousts with the Black Bonanza.

By 1861 the Venango was a mad valley. Derricks were going up everywhere as oil hunters probed for oil. Hastily built hotels were crammed full, two in every bed. Everywhere mud was the nightmare of the oil men. Steam engines were huffing all over the valley; great piles of barrels in which to ship the oil were stacked along Oil Creek, which was so shallow

that horses walking in the stream bed drew the oil-laden barges. Several great flowing wells had come in, pouring out their liquid wealth. One on the Rouse lease farther down Oil Creek came in with a flow of 3,000 barrels a day, spurting oil over the derrick and surrounding territory. Suddenly a terrific explosion set fire to the well and the surrounding buildings, fatally burning several spectators, including the owner of the lease. It was merely the first of the great oil fires threatening the area. Prices of land and for leases soared to fantastic figures. Oil was still selling for $10 per barrel.

By 1861 Lyman Stewart had saved up enough for a second plunge in oil. He and several partners leased the Boyd farm near Petroleum Center. This time, profiting from experience, they saved out $1,000 to drill a well. Their first well was a producer. But just as it came in, with fortune again at their fingertips, several other new wells likewise began spewing out more oil than the buyers could handle. The bottom dropped out of the market. The price of oil fell so low that Stewart and his partners could not afford to pump oil. Again they lost their lease. Later, the Boyd Farm lease became one of the valley's richest producers, but not for Lyman Stewart.

The market for oil became more hazardous. The Venango Valley had the oil, but people throughout the world hadn't learned to use it. The *Venango Spectator*, the valley's leading newspaper, commented in 1862:

"The great depression in the market prices of crude petroleum in the past year, while it has almost ruined all the operators of limited means or forced them to seek more remunerative businesses, has also been the means of introducing the product to all parts of the world, and made it as much a necessity as any single article of human want. As an illuminator it is beyond the reach of competition. Its brilliancy is unsurpassed, and its cheapness unparalleled, even at double the present ruling prices."

By 1861 Europe began to be a major outlet for Pennsylvania oil. The outbreak of the Civil War cut this market off. Putting aside the dreams of riches from oil, Lyman Stewart joined a group of volunteers from the valley and enlisted in the 16th Pennsylvania Cavalry. The young tanner-oil man spent most of the next four years as a valet to horses, with the rank of private. His one claim to military distinction was that his unit was at Appomattox Courthouse when General Robert E. Lee surrendered to General Ulysses S. Grant, ending the war.

Returning to Titusville in 1865, Stewart could scarcely believe his eyes. A village of 400 people in 1859 had grown to a population of over 6,000 and was still rapidly increasing. Titusville had

*Oil-carrying fleet of barges and steamboats rendezvous about 1860 at junction of Oil Creek and Allegheny River below Titusville, Pennsylvania. Pipelines and tank cars replaced barges.*

*Muddy "bottomless" roads through early Pennsylvania oil fields near Lyman Stewart's home so impressed him he later spearheaded drive to cover nation's highways with asphalt.*

thirteen hotels, so crowded with guests that a large percentage of the customers had only half a bed, an entire interest in a bed being a thing unknown in the oil fields. The town had three banks, fat with profits from oil operations. A new and handsome reading room had opened, well supplied with papers and periodicals of the day. The Titusville "Opera House" attracted a constant stream of lecturers, singers, and musicians. The railroad had been built south from Corry, 27 miles away, and extended through Titusville to Oil City on the Allegheny River.

Pipelines now transported the oil to the shipping centers, and the hundreds of tough, cursing mule skinners whose teams formerly transported the oil over the muddy bottomless roads had departed. The waters of shallow Oil Creek had been dammed. Fleets of flat boats and barges carrying from 1,000 to 3,000 barrels of oil swooshed down Oil Creek on the crests of artificial freshets when the spillways were opened. Steamboats picked up the oil at Oil City and transported it down the Allegheny River to Pittsburgh. The railroads had devised tank cars to haul the products of the refineries, largely kerosene, to the Atlantic seaboard. Thousands of derricks dotted the valley, and thousands of wells were spewing out oil,

20

*Pioneer Run, Pennsylvania, about the time Lyman Stewart settled there to begin buying and selling leases, aided by knowledge of the countryside gained as a tanner's apprentice.*

more oil than the markets could absorb.

Lacking capital but more determined than ever to shake himself from the life of a tanner, young Stewart undertook to round out his meager education with a hurry-up commercial course at Eastman's Business College in Poughkeepsie, New York. Though his funds were exhausted at the end of six months, he managed by deep concentration to digest the course. It stood him in good stead. All his life Lyman Stewart was sharp with figures. Back in the valley, he opened an office on Pioneer Run, not far from Titusville, dabbling in oil leases. His boyhood experience tramping over the hills, collecting

hides and delivering the leather, became an unexpected asset. He knew the valley as well as or better than almost any other operator.

Stewart's lot took a turn for the better. Hardly had he opened his office than a boom hit Pioneer Run. One well came in for 600 barrels a day. Speculators and promoters, financiers and drillers came in. Lyman Stewart was ready for them; negotiating leases with the farmers, he began to make money. Oil was a hazardous game. Pit Hole, one of the strikes of the valley, proved that. A wildcat well flowing 250 barrels a day came in one January. Speculators stampeded into the

21

neighborhood, and by September the Pit Hole field was producing 6,000 barrels a day. Pit Hole mushroomed into a boom town with several banks, 50 hotels, the third largest post office in the state, and a population of 15,000. Then the wells began to go dry, pumped out. New ones failed to yield. The exodus started, and in a few months the new homes, banks, hotels, and other structures were vacant. Pit Hole became a ghost oil city.

From Pit Hole, Lyman Stewart learned a lesson in financing on a shoestring, one that he practiced the rest of his life. He began to buy one-sixty-fourth interests in wells that were being sunk, thus spreading his meager capital over a maximum of chances. Later he was able to increase this to one-thirty-seconds, and eventually to eighths. But he and his older brother Milton, with whom he operated in partnership, always tried to spread their risks as far as possible. By 1868 the Stewarts were known as well-established young operators. They also had a unique reputation that set them apart from the typical rowdy, rough-and-ready oil-boom crowd.

"The Stewarts, even then, were known as gentlemen," recalls one of their Titusville contemporaries. "They dressed immaculately. They were courteous and soft-spoken. A profane word never came from their lips. Milton was not much of a mixer. He stuck close to the financial and refining end. Lyman could go out into the roughest and toughest field and mix with the most foul-mouthed scum and riffraff and command the respect of everyone. He was never a hypocrite. He carried his faith with him, and the roughest characters seemed to respect him, not only for his knowledge of oil but for his cleanliness and downright decency. All of the Stewarts were Christian gentlemen, and of them all Lyman was the most respected and beloved."

In 1867 occurred an incident which not only illustrated Lyman's character but also affected his fortune, bringing him to the attention of Frank W. Andrews, one of the most aggressive operators in the area. Along with Andrews and several others, the Stewart brothers were watching a new well being torpedoed to increase the flow of oil. As the explosive cut loose, it blasted out a tremendous volume of petroleum, drenching most of the spectators with the foul-smelling liquid. While others cursed and fumed, Milton turned to Lyman, gazed at his brother's drenched white suit, and quietly began to rub the oil off the clothing.

"Quite a bit of oil," commented Milton.

"Yes, and it's good oil," said Lyman as he fingered it. "The well should be a good producer."

Not a word was said about the oil-bespattered suits. This composure so impressed Andrews that when, a little later, he formed the Claremont Oil Company at Petroleum Center, the Stewart brothers were invited to take an interest. As one

*Tallman Farm near Titusville, Pennsylvania, gave Lyman Stewart his first oil fortune. Also shown are the Sheridan and Atkinson Farms as they appeared about 1868.*

22

of the eight partners who put up $21,000 cash to buy at a sheriff's sale a 90-acre farm, which later became one of the big oil producers, Lyman Stewart made a substantial fortune from the transaction. A few weeks later Andrews came to them with another proposition, this time to buy a five-eighths interest in the 112-acre Tallman farm. Within two years oil from wells on this farm had sold for $800,000.

The Stewart luck had changed. It appeared as though nothing could go wrong with the brothers' plunges in oil. In the six years from 1866 to 1872, Lyman Stewart accumulated close to $300,000 cash in the bank. He and Milton were holders of shares in many wells. Milton Stewart had branched out into a small refinery. Lyman stuck to the producing end. He was also head of Lyman Stewart & Company, a family partnership

through which the Stewarts participated in many oil deals. In 1870 Lyman, feeling that he should be nearer to the scene of his most active operation, the Tallman farm, built himself a substantial two-story frame house at Shamburg. He was already a substantial family man, having married on May 2, 1867, Sarah Adelaide Burrows, a devout and religious young New Yorker whose family had settled in Cherrytree a decade before. In this house Will, second of their four children, was born.

Then in 1871 another apparently insignificant incident changed the course of Lyman Stewart's life. While the brothers were riding the crest of the wave, Milton invited Lyman to a meeting of the Mendelssohn Society of Titusville, which had gone in a big way for culture. Unfortunately Lyman had to meet a man. Milton and his friends had an evening of music,

24

and about midnight decided to organize a little oil company among themselves to take over a small lease Milton knew they could get. They named their new concern the Octave Oil Company. With this musical beginning the company made some money. But none of it went to Lyman, who was forgotten when the partnership was set up.

Lyman had spent the evening with a persuasive visitor from Corry, a character with a glib tongue and a big idea, namely, to establish a factory to build and sell agricultural machinery. Lyman and another newly rich oil man agreed to underwrite the project. This he felt he could well afford to do; he had an income of around a thousand dollars a week and $300,000 cash in the bank. He was a charter member of the Titusville Oil Exchange, the first exchange of its kind in the world. He had been a leading figure in the producers' committee to study conservation and to guard against overproduction. Lyman Stewart was known in the fields as "a man who knows oil." Had he stayed with the business he knew, he would have saved himself years of financial heartbreak. As it was, the agricultural implement business was a complete failure. Lyman Stewart and his friend had to pay off the losses, and when they were through Lyman was not only flat broke but had lost his home and most of his oil leases. By 1872 he was forced to take a job at a small wage to provide for his family.

While Lyman Stewart was in the $1,-000-a-week bracket, he had befriended a number of young field men, among them James and Harvey Hardison, two brothers from Maine. The Hardisons had come to the Pennsylvania oil fields shortly after Drake's discovery well touched off the boom, and had hired out as laborers to get drilling experience. Eventually they became experts at fishing for lost tools in oil wells. Several times they came to Lyman Stewart's home to discuss mechanical problems with him. Even then he had revealed an engineering knowledge surprising in a man with so limited an education. When the brothers needed money, Lyman Stewart dug into his bank account. Although he had helped them set themselves up in business, he never profited financially from the Hardison connection, although he picked up what proved to be, in later years, an invaluable friendship.

Out West another Hardison brother, Wallace, was piling up a small fortune cutting ties for a new transcontinental railroad. When he returned East with his profits, Wallace stopped off at Titusville to look things over. His brothers had written to him about the kindness of their friend Lyman Stewart, so Wallace Hardison hunted up Stewart to get acquainted.

*Lyman Stewart built this family home at Shamburg. Mrs. Lyman Stewart (Sara Adelaide Burrows) is seated on steps while her husband holds their son, William Lyman, destined to succeed his father as president of Union Oil. The family was forced to give up this home and move back to Titusville when Stewart lost his money in an ill-fated venture.*

*Millions of dollars in oil revenues poured through this simple structure near Shamburg while Lyman Stewart was receiving an income of $1,000 a week as one of eight partners who held a lease on part of the Tallman Farm acreage.*

Impressed by the opportunities in the oil game, Hardison proposed that he and Lyman Stewart buy some more properties on a partnership basis. Virtually penniless at the time, Stewart explained his embarrassed estate and expressed his regret that he couldn't join in the enterprise. Wallace Hardison brushed the protests aside.

"You know oil and I don't," he said. "I have the money and you don't. We'll be partners. I'll put up the money and you put up the experience."

On that basis, with only a handclasp to seal the agreement, began a partnership that was never put in formal written agreement until many years later in California, when it had grown to such an enormous business that the bankers considered a written agreement necessary. The partners always addressed each other as "Mr.

26

Hardison" and "Mr. Stewart" throughout their long association.

The new start in the oil business restored Lyman Stewart's old confidence. No longer on a hand-to-mouth existence, he tackled some of the problems of getting more and more oil from the earth. His studies led to a series of inventions which played an important part in the technical development of the infant industry.

In April, 1875, Lyman Stewart filed his first application for a patent on "an improvement in oil wells," which had to do with "a novel method for the employment of steam, hot air, or benzine for the removal of kerosene, so called, which may be deposited upon or within the tube or cylinder arranged within an oil well." This first patent was hardly granted when he hit upon an idea for improvement in packing in oil wells. This invention was followed by another, and still another, which made Stewart an important technical man in the oil fields.

One of the men whom Stewart befriended in his plush days was Captain J. T. Jones, a large landholder in the newly developed Bradford field. In the spring of 1877, when the Bradford strikes

*Main street of Shamburg, Pennsylvania, around 1870 where Lyman Stewart moved to be closer to his investments in the nearby Tallman Farm. The Stewart home was located a few hundred yards back of the drugstore.*

were beginning to attract attention, Stewart mentioned them to Hardison, saying that Bradford looked like a good proposition.

"Well, we'll saddle up our horses in the morning and look the country over," said Hardison, who was quick to make decisions and still quicker to act.

So the next day they started on a rough, 100-mile ride to Bradford, where grateful Captain Jones granted them leases on some of his best acreage. Stewart and Hardison got in just ahead of the rush. The Bradford area soon bloomed into the most spectacular oil field of the decade, with 7,000 producing wells turning out 100,000 barrels daily. This one field produced 80 per cent of this country's oil in 1881. Hardison and Stewart made only a modest fortune from their operations there, for the reason that the very plethora of oil led to the doom of the producers. Prices fell as scores of big-yield wells came in and output zoomed. Bradford swamped the country with oil. Big buyers, notably John D. Rockefeller and associates, seized a strangle hold on distribution facilities and markets. They controlled the pipelines, the railroad, and the exchanges, forcing the price of oil at the well down to a low of 8 cents a barrel, less than the cost of pumping.

Lyman Stewart and Wallace L. Hardison talked over the gloomy outlook. Both were fed up with the cutthroat competition. Hardison had branched out into politics, banking, and farming. He had served a session in the Pennsylvania Legislature where he fathered the law that made pipelines common carriers. He

bought a bank and some farms in Eldred and had become a man of many interests.

Lyman Stewart had been intrigued for several years by reports from California on the potential oil fields in the Golden State. When I. E. Blake, a former Titusville boy who had become an important oil operator in California, returned home and told about the great petroleum deposits in Southern California, Stewart made up his mind to investigate them firsthand. Blake, who later became president of two oil companies in California, offered Stewart all the land he could drill if he would come out West. Stewart proposed to Hardison that they sell out and go West. Hardison was unwilling to return to the Pacific Coast, but he did agree to sell out. They realized about $135,000 from their oil investments. Dividing the money, they parted company, Hardison heading for Kansas, Lyman Stewart to go farther west.

Thus it was a veteran operator, seasoned by twenty-four years in the school of hard knocks, who boarded a train at Titusville in the winter of 1882 with his fifteen-year-old son William, bound for California. Mrs. Stewart stayed at home in Titusville until Lyman Stewart could size up the opportunities in California and provide a home for the family.

"What I was to find in the West, I knew not," said Lyman Stewart later, "except that it was opportunity, and that was all I asked. With me I carried the small Bible Mrs. Stewart had given me years before. That Bible was to be my guide and protector, my inspiration during the hectic and discouraging times just ahead."

28

CHAPTER THREE

## California's Black Gold

COMPARED to the lusty Pennsylvania industry he had left behind, Lyman Stewart found California's miniature oil strike little short of puny when he stepped off the dusty train in Los Angeles late in 1882. In a quarter century, California's oil wells had yielded but 504,135 barrels of crude; the Bradford field alone, in which Stewart and Hardison had made their stake, poured forth that much petroleum in a single week. Two of California's three promising fields had already dried up. The Newhall-Ventura area was the only field with dependable wells, and they were insignificant by Pennsylvania standards. The infant Pacific Coast oil boom had fizzed out, leaving a void in the pocketbooks of thousands of speculators, mainly San Franciscans. Though the oil was in Southern California, the money market and the population were in the north.

But the California booster spirit, even then, more than made up what production lacked. Lyman Stewart's old friend I. E.

Blake of the Pacific Coast Oil Company met him and young Will at the depot and assured him, prophetically, as did Blake's exuberant friends, that the Golden State's Black Bonanza was just beginning to disgorge its riches. Hadn't the state's gold mines yielded their first billion? Well, California's oil wells would give even more generously. The oil was there, though Californians had put more money into holes than they had taken out. Two transcontinental railroads were launching a rate war that would almost double the population in two decades. That meant markets, which the Western oil producers needed more than anything else. A new era was dawning, insisted the optimists.

By this time, Lyman Stewart was an experienced, more cautious plunger in oil. Before risking his limited resources, roughly $75,000, he dug into the background of the California oil deal which, as a quarter century of disappointments had revealed, was far from being another Pennsylvania. What he gleaned was this:

29

Tens of thousands of men who fought, starved, and met violent death seeking fortunes in the California Gold Rush of 1849 apparently had overlooked more potential wealth in the Black Bonanza than they could ever have coveted in their wildest flights of fancy. In their craze for gold, the Argonauts paid little attention to this black, evil-smelling tarry substance that oozed from the ground, fouled up small streams, spoiled water wells, and was generally regarded as a nuisance.

Paradoxically, though gold was not discovered until 1848, the far more precious stuff, oil, had been known to Californians for more than a century. It wasn't hidden. It floated on the surface of ponds. It collected in nature-made reservoirs. The oil was there, waiting for man to use his imagination and put it to work.

As in the Pennsylvania area, the Indians were the first users of California's oil. They collected the sticky tar from oil seepages and brea beds, and mended mortars and pestles, cemented basketwork to make it watertight, fastened spearheads onto the wooden shafts, waterproofed granaries for storing their food, and caulked their primitive canoes with it. They even used the lighter oils from the seepages for coughs and colds, for cuts and burns. The coastal Indians traded tar to tribes of the interior for skins and spearheads. Thus, oil was already a commodity of commerce when the white man arrived.

The early Spanish padres, the rancheros, and their vaqueros knew of the oil, but did little about it until 1855, when General Andreas Pico and his nephew Romulo began collecting it from pits in the canyon near Newhall, Southern California, that now bears the Pico name. General Pico, brother of the last Mexican Governor of California, Pio Pico, was the same who had defeated United States General Stephen W. Kearney in 1847, but who was forced to surrender later to General John C. Frémont. General Pico, who later served as state senator, sold the oil at the little mission town of San Fernando for a lubricant, a medicine, or an illuminant.

One year later, an enterprising San Francisco druggist, Charles Morrell, built a small, primitive distilling plant close to the maltha seepages at Carpinteria near Santa Barbara. Morrell refined an illuminant, but failed to make a success of the enterprise. The West was not yet ready for such advanced illumination, and the potential customers balked at the foul smell and the smoke of the kerosene refined from California petroleum.

Already there were a half-dozen camphene stills in and around San Francisco, refining illuminating oil from crude turpentine brought around the Horn from the Carolinas and West Virginia. About 1859, Eastern oil merchants began shipping the new Pennsylvania petroleum kerosene to the Pacific Coast, where they

*Two handsome drillers, David Swartz and Hall Proudfoot, were employed at Tar Creek, California, in 1888 by the Hardison & Stewart Oil Co., predecessor of Union Oil. Equipment from this well has been preserved in the California Oil Museum at Santa Paula.*

sold it for less than the cost of distilling turpentine in San Francisco.

As early as 1846, Thomas A. Larkin, United States consul at Monterey, then capital of Mexican California, had reported "several places throughout California where a bituminous pitch is used to cover the house roofs." Larkin thought this sticky, black mess might have some commercial value, but he wasn't too sure. He was merely reporting his observations to Washington. Nothing happened.

About the time Consul Larkin made his report, George Shoobridge Gilbert was busy developing a whale-oil business in Brooklyn. Gilbert, a native of Kent, England, was brought to the United States by his father at the age of five. Three years later he was an orphan and struck out for himself. By the time of the Gold Rush, he was well established in Brooklyn but, like many others unable to resist the tales of easy wealth in California, he sold his business in 1851 and migrated to San Francisco, reestablishing himself in the sperm-oil trade under the name of Phoenix Oil

*General Andreas Pico of Mexico was one of earliest of California's petroleum pioneers.*

Works. Gilbert refined oil brought in by whalers who hunted the great mammals from Alaska to Hawaii.

More than ordinarily alert in his business, Gilbert soon heard of the oil seepages in Southern California. In 1857, two years before Drake's discovery well set off the petroleum boom in Pennsylvania, Gilbert, aided financially by Charles Hosmer, began distilling "liquid bitumen and asphaltum," first in San Francisco then in a small refinery on the Ojai Ranch near San Buena Ventura, where he managed to produce about 400 barrels of marketable oil. This establishes Gilbert as operator of the first successful commercial petroleum refinery in California.

Soon after Gilbert began distilling California crude, A. C. Ferris, a whale-oil refiner from Brooklyn, called on him. This was before Drake struck oil in Pennsylvania, and Ferris thought this new oil product Gilbert was turning out had commercial possibilities in the East and might even compete with whale oil. So he bought 100 small barrels of Gilbert's oil and shipped it to Panama, thence by mule-back across the Isthmus, after which he planned to transship it to New York by sailing boat. Unfortunately, as Ferris wrote Gilbert, "the cost of the shipment forebade its importation," and the cargo was dumped by the muleteers in the Panamanian jungle, where it was found years later.

Ferris was born forty years too soon. Four decades later, the Union Oil Company of California laid the first trans-Panama pipeline and pumped California crude to the Atlantic Coast while the Panama Canal was being dug.

While Gilbert was busily dipping oil at his Ojai refinery, Professor Benjamin Silliman, Jr., of Yale arrived in 1864 off Southern California via Cape Horn. This was the same Professor Silliman who had analyzed the Titusville crude for the Pennsylvania Rock Oil Company back in 1855. Eager to check reports of California's fabulous oil seepages, Silliman landed at San Buena Ventura, where townspeople told him about Gilbert's liquid bitumen and asphalt refining still up Sulphur Mountain way. The professor immediately hired a horse and headed up the dusty trail to Rancho Ojai.

Delighted that a man of Silliman's

32

*Los Angeles in 1883 when Lyman Stewart reached the city on his first trip West to investigate possibilities of reentering petroleum business along Pacific Coast.*

standing should be so interested, Gilbert pointed out his source of crude, the seepages along San Antonio Creek and on the slopes of Sulphur Mountain. Silliman was fascinated. For days he rode back and forth over the region, scarcely believing what he saw but finally giving in to his own enthusiasm. On July 2, 1864, he wrote to his friend Thomas R. Scott of Philadelphia, that "the property covers an area of 18,000 acres of land in one body, on which there are 20 natural oil wells, some of them of very large size. The oil is struggling to the surface at every available point and is running away down the rivers for miles. Artesian wells will be fruitful along a double line of 13 miles,

say for about 25 miles in linear extent. The ranch is an old Spanish grant of 4 leagues of land, lately confirmed and of perfect title. It has, as I have stated, 18,000 acres of land well watered by four rivers, but its great value is in its almost fabulous wealth in the best oil."

Somewhat as an afterthought he estimated that a net profit of $1,365,000 could be made from drilling 10 wells on the property. That was big talk for a conservative professor.

Tom Scott was one of the wildcatters who had profited fabulously from the Pennsylvania oil boom. He was a partner of Andrew Carnegie and J. E. Thomson in the Story Farm field at Titusville, a

33

strike that yielded tremendous returns. Scott had expanded his holdings all through the Pennsylvania oil district and was ready to put some of his surplus dollars to work elsewhere. Professor Silliman's letter convinced him that out in the West lay the opportunity for another spectacular strike. In fact, if he could believe the enthusiastic reports of the professor, California held an ocean of oil awaiting exploiters to pump it and sell it.

Strangely enough, for a man of Scott's business experience, he overlooked the consideration that the market in the West at that time was extremely limited compared to the heavily populated East. Though he was a busy man, being vice-president of the Pennsylvania Railroad and Assistant Secretary of War in Lincoln's Civil War cabinet, Scott called in a group of friends, laid out a map of California, and read what Professor Silliman had written. Their enthusiasm aroused, Scott and his friends formed a syndicate then and there to purchase not only the Ojai Ranch but other oil properties extending from Humboldt County to Los Angeles.

Three companies were formed by this group to handle the California deals— the Philadelphia and California Petroleum Company, the California Petroleum Company, and the Pacific Coast Petroleum Company. Scott's syndicate purchased a total of 277,000 acres, including the following ranchos: Simi (113,000 acres), Las Posas (26,500 acres), San Francisco (48,000 acres), Calleguas (10,000 acres), Colonia (54,000 acres), Canada Larga (660 acres), and Ojai (16,000

acres); a large part of the town of San Buena Ventura, all in what is now Ventura County; and 12,000 additional acres in Humboldt and Los Angeles counties.

Of the three corporations organized by Scott, only one, the California Petroleum Company, was active. Its prospectus in 1865 announced its capital as 10 million dollars adding that "one-tenth of the stock has been reserved for working capital." Like many early oil companies, it was nine-tenths water, one-tenth oil.

Scott was too busy to take personal charge of this Western venture. So were his associates. Scott called in two nephews, D. C. Scott and Thomas R. Bard, recently discharged from the Union Army. To counsel the young men, inexperienced in oil production, he sent along with them J. A. Beardsley, a pioneer oil man from Titusville.

Bard, whom destiny had marked for first president of the Union Oil Company of California, was in poor health. After plunging into the study of law at seventeen in his home town of Chambersburg, Pennsylvania, he was forced to quit and seek outdoor employment. His Civil War service with the Army Engineers had convinced him that law practice was not his forte. He welcomed the chance to go West.

Bard and his colleagues were told to stop in New York, Bradford, and Titusville to buy what drilling equipment they needed. Knowing little about oil hunting in the Far West, they picked up a steam-drilling rig, the first ever shipped to California.

Drillers were already "making hole" in

34

California's valleys and hills, even before young Bard headed West. Shallow spring-pole wells had been punched down at several points near oil seepages, notably in Humboldt, Marin, Contra Costa, San Mateo, Colusa, and Santa Clara counties. Outside the sleepy town of Los Angeles, a Colonel E. D. Baker was spending thousands of dollars drilling along what was years later to become the Wilshire Boulevard "Miracle Mile" business district, but getting little oil.

The first actual oil well drilled in California was on the Davis Ranch in Humboldt County about 1861. There were hand-dug oil pits before this, but no drilled wells. During the next three years, wells were drilled in various localities— on San Pablo Creek in Contra Costa County, in the McKittrick oil seepages, on the Medar Ranch in Santa Cruz—but no commercial oil production resulted. Boring into the sides of the hills where seepages occurred, so that oil trickling from the sides and roofs of tunnels could flow out by gravity, had proved more productive.

There was oil fever in the air and a feeling of exciting times ahead, when Bard reached California in 1865. From a ship anchored off San Pedro, Bard unloaded equipment such as had never been seen before in the West, drilling tools, casing, a furnace and retort for refining, barrels, and, of all things, three boilers and engines, constituting his steam-drilling outfit. These Bard laboriously carted 100 miles across hills and valleys to Ojai, ironically passing across the greatest oil deposit in California beneath the sands

*Lyman Stewart at the age of thirty-five, when he first became a partner of W. L. Hardison in Pennsylvania.*

on which he unloaded his gear. But as Lyman Stewart discovered later, Bard wasn't alone in passing up the big pools hidden by the Golden State's geologic faults.

Three San Francisco businessmen— Thomas Richards, William Ede, and Edward Bosqui—had just organized the Union Mattole Oil Company and focused oil interest on the Mattole River in Humboldt County. The Humboldt seepages were nearer San Francisco, largest market on the Pacific and the West's financial center, than those of the Ventura area. Humboldt looked like an adequate source of oil. On June 10, 1865, the *Humboldt Times* printed a small but highly significant item:

35

*Los Angeles looked like this about the time Lyman Stewart and W. L. Hardison arrived in California to look for oil. Picture looks west on Temple Street from Bunker Hill. The oil belt which crossed Temple at the top of the grade was developed much later.*

"The first shipment of coal oil from Humboldt County. On Wednesday last, Mr. F. Francis of Ferndale brought into town six packages of from 15 to 20 gallons each of coal oil taken from the well of the Union Mattole Oil Company. This will go to San Francisco by the present trip of the steamer, and is the first oil shipment of crude oil from the oil regions of this county."

This shipment, distilled by the Stanford Brothers at their camphene works on Chestnut and Taylor streets, was the first oil from a drilled well distilled and sold in California, the crude supply used by Gilbert at Ojai having come from seepages rather than drilled wells. The Stanford Brothers firm consisted of Josiah, A. P., and Charles. The brothers began quietly buying up Union Mattole stock and soon

had control of the producing company. Unfortunately for them, the first well drilled on the Union Mattole property was the best one. Others drilled in the area never became good producers.

But California's pioneer oil boom had been touched off. Between 1865 and 1867, when it collapsed, 70 companies capitalized at 45 million dollars had drilled 60 wells. It cost 1 million dollars in hard cash to produce 5,000 barrels of oil worth $10,000.

By 1867, Eastern "coal oil" was selling in San Francisco for 54 cents a gallon, less than the cost of refining and marketing kerosene from California products. Hayward & Coleman, who refined 40,000 gallons of illuminating oil from petroleum springs near Santa Barbara, had to shut down. Transportation from the wells to the refineries and the market was not only

36

costly but time-consuming. One producer in Humboldt County shipped oil in small containers on muleback for 30 or 40 miles to the village of Centerville; there he loaded it onto wagons for another 30-mile haul to Eureka; then it was loaded onto a steamer for the 216-mile trip to San Francisco.

Finally, to complete deflation of the Humboldt boom, the United States government on March 17, 1865, ordered all oil lands in the county withheld from prospecting, thus making most of the leases and titles of dubious value.

In Southern California, Bard, backed by some of the wealthiest oil and businessmen in the East and with 227,000 acres in fee simple on which to drill, was little concerned with the collapse that wiped out rival wildcatters. Early in 1866, he completed his first well, drilling some 500 feet into a brea bed. Bard had located this initial well near the tar beds on the east bank of San Antonio Creek, later renamed the Ventura River. It yielded more water than oil and had to be abandoned. For his second try, he moved the rig about 5 miles upcreek. At 520 feet his drill hit a small quantity of oil, but not enough for commercial exploitation.

By now Bard was convinced that he should drill farther away from the tar beds. For his third hole he chose a spot on Sisar Creek, about 20 miles from San Buena Ventura. He had a theory, later proved to be correct, that if he went deeper his chances of production would be better. So he boldly planned to drill this third well to 1,500 feet. Scott readily agreed with this idea, but the failure of

Bard and Scott to get oil where Silliman had reported it "flowing down the rivers" indicated to the directors of the company in Philadelphia that something was amiss in their California venture. To get unbiased information, they induced two medicine men, Dr. John Torrey and Dr. Charles T. Jackson, who were also reputed to be conversant with mineralogy, to make a trip to California and "examine the property."

The doctors arrived on the scene just as Bard was punching his No. 3 well down around the 520-foot level. They looked the situation over, then looked at No. 1 and No. 2 and "suggested" to Bard and Scott that they abandon the new well. One man's opinion was as good as another's, for no one knew much about California's tricky geology at the time. With the advice of the two medicine men, Bard picked the fourth site some distance away and began drilling anew. He abandoned this well at 400 feet when the visiting braintrusters began shaking their heads.

What had the doctors to suggest now? They rejected Bard's deep-drilling theory and advised the practice of punching holes near seepages. This meant shallow wells which could be drilled by the old spring-pole method, much cheaper than running the steam-drill rigs. The next well produced oil at 100 feet. Not much, but 6 barrels a day was oil, and that was something, and the first oil they had found in salable quantity.

Bard and Scott had learned something, at the price of drilling these first five wells. The drills, the tools, the machinery that easily and speedily banged through the clay soils of Pennsylvania were totally inadequate in the rugged, rocky formations of California's oil fields. In the West, strata were not horizontal, but were upended by the earth's convulsions. Bard concluded that the oil was probably in pockets created by these geologic upheavals.

He decided that he and Scott would pick the next location. Ordering the steam rig back into service, Bard prepared to go down 2,000 feet, if necessary, in a sixth "make-or-break" well. The directors back East were getting more and more apprehensive. Where was all this oil that should have been spurting from the hills and valleys? Racing against time, Bard drove his crew on long shifts, fearing orders to quit drilling before he had tested his theory. When the drill reached 550 feet, far short of his ultimate goal, it struck oil sands, good for 15 to 20 barrels a day of a good grade oil. This was more like it. This was the best well the West had so far produced.

But paralleling Lyman Stewart's experience with his first producing well in Pennsylvania, Bard now had struck a good supply of crude petroleum at the very moment the bottom was dropping out of the market. It no longer paid to produce Western oil. Refining cost more than the Eastern refiners charged for better products delivered in San Francisco. It was now late in 1866 and the country was in the throes of the post–Civil War depression. Bard had spent around $200,000 hunting oil on lands where it was reportedly flowing down the creeks. Out of six

wells, he had two commercial producers but no market for his oil.

From Philadelphia Colonel Scott issued orders that all further drilling cease immediately. This touched off similar retrenchment by other operators. By the close of 1866, every oil company in the state except one had either shut down or gone out of business. The exception was the Union Mattole Oil Company, which the Stanford Brothers had recently purchased. They were forced to do some token drilling "to safeguard their land titles." The California oil bubble had burst.

While Bard and Scott were drilling on Ojai Ranch, Josiah Stanford, a mining man and brother of the railroad builder, became interested in the oil seepages of Sulphur Mountain. With his mining experience he decided to drive tunnels into the south slope of the mountain to intercept an oil-sand formation estimated to be 16 miles long. Stanford dug his tunnel in 80 feet, with the floor so inclined that the oil flowed out by gravity into tanks near the entrance. This gave him economical production. Some 31 tunnels were driven into Sulphur Mountain during the next quarter century. Stanford gleaned from 1 to 20 barrels a day from each of his tunnels. For a time he was one of California's leading oil producers.

It was 1870 before oil fever revived in California. That year Sanford Lyon rigged up a spring-pole outfit and punched a hole at the head of Pico Canyon. He got some oil, but not enough to arouse excitement. An enterprising dealer managed to ship 97 barrels out of San Pedro in 1873. Interest in oil was gradually awakening.

38

Others moved into Pico Canyon. Colonel E. D. Baker drilled a shallow well near Lyon's first hole and got 6 barrels a day at 90 feet. There was still no real excitement and still not much production.

Out from Pennsylvania in 1873 came C. C. Mentry, a heavy-set, heavily bearded carpenter who had built dozens of derricks around Titusville, then had become a driller. Oil leases were a "dime a dozen" in California, so Mentry picked up one alongside the Baker well. Using the spring-pole method, Mentry sank a hole and found oil only 30 feet down. The well yielded only 2 barrels a day, but when Mentry went deeper to 76 feet he tripled the output. Encouraged, he drilled another well across the canyon and, from about the same depth, got about the same production. He was hitting oil. He hurried in to Los Angeles and signed up a lease for 25 acres between Well No. 1 and Well No. 2. Now he would really start producing oil. His third well was a dry hole.

This might have ended Mentry in California's oil picture but for the timely appearance of D. G. Scofield, Lyman Stewart's old schoolmate from Titusville. Scofield left Pennsylvania with considerably more experience than dollars. Reaching San Francisco, he discovered that while most of the petroleum financing

*Jackline equipment is still used on some Union Oil leases near Santa Paula. Chain-and-sprocket pumping device (below) is on Adams 27 in Wild Bill Canyon. Wooden jack (above) is on the Robertson lease.*

39

*D. G. Scofield, Lyman Stewart's schoolmate, became an active competitor in California.*

of the sixties centered in that city, the actual oil-producing areas were far to the south, around Ventura and Newhall. Scofield worked southward, listening intently to the gossip about oil, taking his time, looking the country over. To his trained eyes Pico Canyon appeared to have the best oil lands he had seen. He was especially impressed with the Mentry property, about which he wrote to W. E. Youle, a drilling contractor back in Pennsylvania.

Scofield reported his findings to a group of influential San Franciscans, among them A. J. Bryant, later mayor, Mark McDonald, Captain James McDonald, and J. A. Scott, a prosperous refiner from Titusville. This group then organized the California Star Oil Company, with Scofield as head. Mentry assigned his leases

to the new company and went on the payroll as drilling superintendent.

Scofield outfitted Mentry with a steam rig and ordered full-speed drilling on a new well, known as Pico No. 4. With this heavier equipment Mentry pushed the well down to 600 feet, where he struck an oil flow of 150 barrels a day. This was the best well so far drilled in California. This production, spectacular at the time, inspired J. A. Scott to erect on the Southern Pacific tracks at Newhall a new and up-to-date refinery, into which he poured all the know-how he had gleaned as a refiner in Titusville. To handle the increasing amount of oil from Pico No. 4 and other wells on the Mentry lease, a 5-mile pipeline, 2 inches in diameter, was laid from the field to the refinery in 1879. It was the first oil pipeline west of the Mississippi.

Here on the precipitous slopes of Pico Canyon the Pacific Coast's oil industry was undergoing a rebirth, this time with a much firmer footing. There was drilling activity anew on the Rancho Ex-Mission de San Buena Ventura on the coast; the Los Angeles Oil Company was organized to develop 800 acres of most interesting oil-seepage land in the Little Sespe district of Ventura County.

While Scofield was checking California oil prospects upon his arrival from the East, he was impressed with the good prospects of Moody Gulch, in the Santa Cruz mountains of Santa Clara County. Not so promising as those of Pico Canyon, they were nevertheless worth testing. His friend Youle had arrived from Titusville. They looked over the Moody Gulch area together. Seepages convinced them that the Gulch, only 60 miles from the San

40

Francisco market, should be prospected as soon as drilling equipment could be spared from Pico Canyon.

While Scofield and Youle were tramping Moody Gulch together, another Pennsylvanian, R. C. McPherson, joined the newly organized San Francisco Oil Company. McPherson drilled a wildcat well in Pico Canyon, a short distance from the California Star wells. This turned out to be a dry hole. McPherson's "duster" influenced the directors of California Star to cease drilling in that area, despite the good production of their earlier wells, and move their rigs north to Moody Gulch. When Scofield and Youle reached the Gulch, they found McPherson had beaten them to the punch with leases to the lands on which they wanted to drill.

McPherson had teamed up with a Colonel Boyer, owner of the San Jose Gas Works, who wanted Moody Gulch oil for his gas business. The partners soon fell into violent disagreement. One day when McPherson came blustering into Boyer's office, the latter reached into his desk, pulled out a six-shooter, and "invited" McPherson to sign over his half interest in the Moody Gulch leases. Persuaded, McPherson grabbed a pen and signed. The Moody Gulch leases were now owned 100 per cent by Boyer. McPherson retired.

Boyer next asked Youle, as an experienced driller, to sink some wells for him. Youle, still obligated to Scofield, hesitated about drilling for Boyer; but Scofield, having no immediate work for Youle, told

*Original still of the Scott & Baker pioneer refinery at Newhall, California, in 1875.*

him to go ahead. From this episode is recorded a good picture of drillers' problems of the period. Youle later wrote:

"I ordered lumber and rig timbers sawed at a mill in the Santa Cruz mountains, some 7 miles away. I purchased a boiler, engine, and tools that were stored in San Francisco—a secondhand outfit but in very good condition. The largest bit was 8 inches; the rig had originally been used to drill a deep water well. I purchased several sizes of pipe from George W. Gibbs, an iron merchant of San Francisco. Then I located a 1,500-foot coil of drilling cable and sand line—they were Manila. The bits I had made by Charles Oester, on Mission Street, San Francisco, and it was certainly some job to make the forgers understand what oil tool work required."

Then Youle got together a crew, only one of whom had ever had any oil experience. Eventually he brought in a well at 700 feet with daily production of 20 barrels. His second well produced 30 barrels a day at 1,700 feet. Moody Gulch looked like a real strike, but it soon turned into a mirage.

Meanwhile wildcatters were drilling in other areas. Near Whittier, 14 miles southeast of Los Angeles, two 1,700-foot wells were drilled and abandoned when the quantity of oil found was too small for commercial production. In Kern County, near McKittrick, another well owned by Sol Jewett was shut in because the oil was too heavy to use. At Glendora the drillers went down 200 feet and got nothing. The Los Angeles Oil Company had secured some reasonably good production in the Little Sespe district and was piping it to

the new refinery at Ventura where E. A. Edwards, the owner, was doing a constantly increasing business extracting kerosene for the Los Angeles market and lubricating oil for San Francisco.

Scofield talked oil prospects so eloquently that United States Senator Charles N. Felton and his close associate Lloyd Tevis, president of the Wells Fargo Bank in San Francisco, finally became interested in the California Star Oil Company. Scofield conducted a group of capitalists through Pico Canyon and Moody Gulch. Senator Felton, impressed by what he saw at Pico, was even more interested in Moody Gulch, nearer to the San Francisco market.

With Senator Felton as front man, backed by the enthusiasm of Scofield, the Pacific Coast Oil Company was incorporated September 9, 1878, for a million dollars. The California Star Oil Company, the San Francisco Oil Company, Colonel Boyer's Santa Clara Oil Company, and several smaller oil concerns were merged into the strong, well-financed outfit that became the giant of the Western oil industry.

More money was still being poured into the ground by Californians than was being taken out in oil. The state's entire production in this year of 1879 was only 19,858 barrels which sold for $39,716.

Two wells, drilled on Pescadero Creek in San Mateo County, were abandoned at 1,000 feet because "the formation was badly faulted, with showing of heavy tar oil all the way down." At Sargent Station, in Santa Clara County, another well was abandoned at 600 feet when the experts decided the heavy asphaltic-base oil it

42

was yielding could not be put to profitable use. At Santa Paula and Sespe Canyon shallow wells were being drilled next to the tar beds, and while some production was hit, the crude was so heavy it was difficult to handle.

Early in the spring of 1880, with the arrival of heavy rigs from the East, the Pacific Coast Oil Company sank several new wells in Pico Canyon and nearby Wiley Canyon. By July the company was ready to go into Moody Canyon in a big way. I. E. Blake, Lyman Stewart's friend who had joined the company to take charge of transportation of the petroleum products, had persuaded Scofield to order 50 tank cars. Blake also proposed that in the Moody Gulch operation the company follow the Pennsylvania practice of contracting the drilling to outsiders. There was only one flaw in the plan, the shortage of drillers in California with experience in the heavy steam rigs. Blake made a trip East to talk more Pennsylvania drillers into trying their luck in California. It was during this visit to Titusville that he planted the urge to go West in Lyman Stewart's mind.

Blake persuaded Daniel Dull, a veteran Eastern driller, to come out West and bid on the Pacific Coast Oil Company drilling. W. E. Youle feared that Dull, experienced only with the easy-to-drill clay fields of Pennsylvania and unfamiliar with the tricky, treacherous California formations, would underbid him. To his surprise, Dull quoted a higher price. So each driller was given half of the wells. Youle and Dull promptly got together, pooled their resources, and contracted together to drill all the wells the

*One of the first wells drilled by Thomas Bard at Rancho Ojai, California, in the sixties.*

Pacific Coast Oil Company proposed to sink at Moody Gulch.

The first well exceeded expectations, coming in for 100 barrels a day. The next five were almost as good. Senator Felton

43

and his associates authorized Scofield to build a 500-barrel-capacity refinery at Alameda Point on San Francisco Bay, from which to ship products to Mexico, British Columbia, Hawaii, and other Pacific ports. All of the company's crude was being delivered in its own 50 tank cars from Newhall and Santa Cruz to Alameda Point. The Pacific Coast Oil Company was largely responsible for the state's production in 1880 of 40,552 barrels, valued at $60,828, a significant increase over the 19,858 barrels of the previous year, but still far behind the $20,030,761 worth of gold bullion dug that year.

Then something happened. Production at Moody Gulch, for some unaccountable reason, fell off abruptly. New wells were hurriedly drilled. Shortly the new wells yielded no more petroleum. The one oil source close to the lucrative San Francisco market was washed up. The costly pipeline and other facilities Felton had authorized were useless, for Moody Gulch had no more oil.

Felton and Scofield called in Youle and Dull and told them to rush their drilling equipment south to Pico and Wiley canyons. "Get us oil and get it fast," were the orders.

Youle and Scofield picked sites for a score of new wells. The drilling was unusually successful, and production rose to 200, then 300, finally 500 barrels a day.

Then the company ran into a new problem. Shipping its crude from the Ventura-Pico-Newhall district to its refinery at Alameda by rail, the oil men were running up prohibitive freight bills. Scofield waged a vigorous campaign to get the Southern Pacific to reduce "excessive" rates on petroleum. The Scott-built refinery at Newhall had shut down, and the company was at the mercy of the railroad to get its crude to the refinery on San Francisco Bay.

One day Southern Pacific officials learned that Felton and Scofield had secretly ordered many miles of pipe and were laying a pipeline from Newhall to Ventura, from which point they could move oil by water to San Francisco. At first the railroad thought they were bluffing. The oil men went on laying pipe. The strategy worked. Before they could complete the pipeline, the railroad "rechecked its figures" and found that freight rates on oil could be cut in half. Felton and Scofield never finished their pipeline nor the tankers they had designed to handle the oil when it reached the ocean end of the pipeline. Thus the distinction of building the first pipeline to tidewater and the first tanker to sail the Pacific went to another pioneer who was winding up his oil business in Pennsylvania. He was Lyman Stewart, whose inventive pioneering was about to revolutionize the adolescent California oil industry.

# CHAPTER FOUR

# *Free Enterprise on a Borrowed Shoestring*

IN retrospect, it is hard to see how the founders of the Union Oil Company survived their early years in California's oil fields. It would be hard to find two free-enterprisers who started with higher hopes than Lyman Stewart and Wallace Hardison, yet who were plagued by worse luck or more formidable dollar troubles. For years they operated not only on a shoestring but a borrowed shoestring that the lenders were always calling back. Only grit and chronic optimism, plus a genius for popping up with new ideas, kept them afloat. Though they were licked time after time, they never seemed to know it. Their achievement in putting together one of the country's great oil empires is a striking drama of opportunity in a free-enterprise world.

No sooner had Lyman Stewart, accompanied by fifteen-year-old Will, landed in Los Angeles in the winter of 1882–1883 than he began encountering old friends from the Pennsylvania oil fields. It was like going to a Titusville picnic in the Los Angeles sunshine. There was D. G. Scofield, his old schoolmate who left Titusville in 1870 to open a paint and hardware store in San Francisco, but who, unable to resist the fascination of the Black Bonanza, returned to the oil game, organizing the California Star Oil Company, later merged into the Pacific Coast Oil Company. There was C. A. Mentry, the Titusville carpenter who made a great reputation as an expert builder of drilling derricks and who later became a driller as well. There was W. E. Youle, also of Titusville, a well-known drilling contractor. There was J. A. Scott, several times a partner with Lyman and Milton Stewart in developing leases in the Bradford area and now owner of a refinery at Newhall. Most important in Lyman Stewart's future was I. E. Blake of the Pacific Coast Oil Company, who had promised all the land Stewart wanted to drill upon in California.

By way of making good his promise,

45

*William Lyman Stewart was fifteen years old when he and his father left Pennsylvania.*

Blake took Stewart up to the Newhall district and pointed out the lands his company held under lease. He offered Stewart the choice of any of them. Stewart had heard all about the problems of drilling for oil in California. Drillers had to punch their holes through hard, solid rock; they banged into geologic faults which diverted the drills and made holes crooked; the oil, if they found it, was heavier and blacker and more viscous than that in Pennsylvania. It was hard to lift out of the pools and difficult to transport, refine, and market. After a survey of Pico Canyon, Stewart returned to Los Angeles to think it over. He went back to the oil fields twice and longed to talk things over with his old partner Wallace Hardison, now beginning life anew as a rancher in Kansas. He wished Hardison could join him. The more he looked about, the more enthusiastic he became. After his third trip to Pico Canyon, he had another meeting with Blake, who again told him to take his pick of the locations from the extensive unproved holdings of the Pacific Coast Oil Company.

Lyman Stewart could hold his enthusiasm in check no longer. There was oil up there, and he yearned to start drilling. He wired Hardison in Kansas, asking if the latter was interested in joining anew in an oil hunt, this time in California. Less than

*Lyman Stewart left Pennsylvania at forty-two to begin a new oil career in California.*

46

a day after he sent his wire, a message came back from Hardison saying he was back in Pennsylvania settling up his affairs. In his usual crisp manner, Hardison asked no questions but merely gave the date on which he would arrive in Los Angeles to start operations. That was all the negotiating or conferring the pair did to launch their partnership in the oil business again.

While Hardison was in Pennsylvania, he bought two heavy drilling rigs and recruited a crew of experienced drillers from around Bradford. These he dispatched westward to reach Los Angeles early in 1883.

Meantime, Lyman Stewart selected a site for their initial hole, picking a location on Christian Hill in Pico Canyon, where there had been no previous drilling. This the partners subleased from the Pacific Coast Oil Company. By the time they were ready to spud in their first well, early in 1883, the two had scraped together $70,000 worth of equipment and enough cash to raise their total capital to $135,000. It seemed like a lot of money, but they soon needed much more.

High in hopes, both Hardison and Stewart were on hand when the drillers started punching down Well No. 1, known in their logs as "Hill No. 1" because of its location on Christian Hill. The Pennsylvanians soon found that they were battling with new formations. They had trouble keeping the hole straight; they were going down a lot deeper than they had

*"Foot-of-the-hill No. 1" as drilling started in 1890 for the Hardison & Stewart Oil Co.*

ever drilled wells back in Pennsylvania. They drilled with enthusiasm until they hit the 1,850-foot level, an unusually deep job for those days. There they ran into real trouble. Their tools were lost, and they were unable to fish them out. All the way down there had been no showing of oil of any kind. The partners decided to chalk it up to experience. Well No. 1 was abandoned.

It was their first dry hole in California. They moved the rig 475 feet to the east and started down again. Hill No. 2 was a replica of Hill No. 1, except that trouble began at 1,050 feet, where the drilling tools were again lost. The partners abandoned this well without seeing a trace of oil. For Hill No. 3, they moved 700 feet west of Hill No. 1 and pushed the hole to the depth of 1,650 feet. Here they found

a trace of oil, but nothing more. So Hill No. 3 was written off as another dry hole. Hill No. 4 was also a duster.

Four dry holes in a row, enough to discourage anyone, especially with funds beginning to run low. "This certainly can't go on," said Hardison. "The law of averages, if nothing else, should work in our favor pretty soon." The partners spudded in Well No. 5. It, too, was a dry hole. Disaster faced the partnership. After all, they didn't have unlimited resources, as they knew only too well when they checked nightly after paying the drilling crews. Well, they had a few thousand dollars left, enough for one more try. Where to drill was the question.

They moved away from Christian Hill, which had swallowed almost all their cash resources, figuring that over on Tar Creek

*Robertson Well No. 1 at Bardsdale in 1890. Standing, left to right: Ed Scholl and two children, John Millard, Ben Robertson, Ed Elkins and an unidentified visitor. Seated, left to right: E. E. Chamberlain, Charley Millard, unidentified, Robert Cruson and son, Tom.*

*Among the early employees of the Hardison & Stewart Oil Company were these men. Back row: Briggs Dougherty, Ed McCray, John Millard, David Swartz, O. C. Parker, and George Fleisher. Center: F. E. Davis, C. N. Baker, John Irwin, Lewis Hardison. Bottom: T. O. Toland, Charles Hazelton, Dick Whitten, E. Wiseman, Link Gilger.*

or Santa Paula Creek they might find more promising spots. This time they had to be right, so it took some time to decide which site they would choose for this final hole. While they were deciding, they asked their drillers to work for a short time at road builders' wages instead of the higher pay commanded by drillers. They had brought the crews out from Pennsylvania, paying their way and guaranteeing them six months' work. The six months were over, and the partners figured that the crews would cooperate to that extent. To their surprise, in the midst of all of their other troubles, the drillers walked off the job, refusing to work for road builders'

wages, even temporarily. So the partners had to go on paying the higher wages and watch their already slender capital grow smaller and smaller day by day, while they worked out the deal for drilling their sixth well, known as "Smith Farm No. 1" on Tar Creek.

The original logbook, still extant, bears mute testimony to the heartache of the twain while that well was being drilled. It reads:

"July 20, 1883. Smith Farm No. 1. Crew: John Irwin, superintendent; David Swartz, George W. Fleisher, William Esner, David Brown. Commence work July 20, 1883. Commence spudding in the

49

Water, hauled in wagons such as this, was sometimes worth more per barrel than oil.

Santa Paula in 1888, with refinery of the Mission Transfer Company at extreme left.

pools July 31. August 6, cased with 119 feet of 8⅝-inch casing. We had a good deal of hard drilling and lost lots of time with crooked holes. At 672 feet, we struck oil rock, and went through at 1,338 feet and got sulphur water that flowed over the top. We tubed the well and pumped for a week, getting lots of water and about 1½ barrels of oil per day. We pulled the tubing and started to drill again. The total depth reached was 1,520 feet. The sides caved badly. There were 282 feet of black slate. The rope broke and left the tools in the well, and it caved in on them. We fished for three weeks and couldn't recover them. We abandoned the well on December 31, 1883, leaving 100 feet of 8⅝ casing in it."

It was New Year's Eve at the end of 1883, a year of stark financial disaster for Lyman Stewart and W. L. Hardison in California. They had drilled six wells and had yet to produce their first barrel of salable oil. They had spent just about every cent they owned, but they still had their drilling rigs and they had plenty of courage, plus the optimism that goes with oil fever. They needed it, for darker days were still ahead.

In desperation, the partners moved the rig over to a spot on Santa Paula Creek. Oil simply couldn't elude them any longer, they figured, probably forgetting that one of their friends, Captain J. T. Jones of Bradford, had drilled 13 consecutive dry holes along Oil Creek in Pennsylvania. They couldn't stop now. Their new well, Santa Paula No. 1, was another dry hole, the seventh in a row for these experienced Pennsylvania oil men.

The partners took stock of the situation. Now they were in dire straits. They had exhausted their capital. Hardison, who had organized two small banks, one at Eldred, Pennsylvania, and the other at Salina, Kansas, had borrowed to the limit. He had drawn so many checks on the Eldred bank that the cashier was protesting in almost every mail, and warning that the depositors were getting wind of Hardison's overdrafts. On May 8 the cashier wrote: "We have had a run on the bank." A few days later he warned: "We must have some funds from some source soon. We have about $10,000 falling due this month, $7,000 of which is yours, due the 25th. The stockholders who are borrowers must come to the front, and do that quickly, or we shall follow in the grand collapse."

Obviously there was no help available from Pennsylvania sources, so Stewart went to his friend Blake and laid their troubles on the table, holding nothing back. He pointed out that they had drilled so far in territory yet to be proven as oil land. They had done a wildcatting job, a costly wildcatting job with seven failures to their record. He asked Blake to give them a chance to drill somewhere in proved territory. They might be able to scrape together enough wages for one more try.

Blake, who had initiated the whole adventure, through his glowing tales of the California oil strikes during his visit to Titusville in 1882, was sympathetic. He knew both Hardison and Stewart were substantial, hard-working, experienced oil men who had simply run into an extraordinarily extended period of bad luck.

"The Star lease (the California Star Oil

51

*One of the first refinery crews employed at Santa Paula by Union Oil Company.*

Works Company) looks like it might be a good thing," said Blake. "Suppose you and Hardison drill your next well over there."

This lease was also in Pico Canyon, but some distance from the site of the first five dusters drilled by the partners. They took a sublease on a small site barely large enough for a single well. It was their last chance. If this failed, they were through. They spudded in a well, known in the logbooks as "Star No. 1." It was an important well in California oil history, because without it the Union Oil Company of California might never have been born.

Desperately racing against time as their meager funds ran out, the partners watched every minute as the drill chipped and chopped its way downward. At 1,620 feet, the bit hit oil. For 30 more feet it continued through the impregnated oil sands. When they pulled out the drilling equipment and put on the pump, it produced 75 barrels a day. They had oil, in an unusually good well for those days in California. They took more oil in a day from that one well than they had recovered in a year from seven other holes. It looked like their luck had changed at last.

52

"We were elated. We had finally struck oil," recalled Stewart later. "But that was about all. Our resources were gone. We didn't have enough funds left to develop the oil we had found in Star No. 1."

The partners tried to get more proved land from the California Star Oil Works Company, on which to drill more wells, but were turned down. If there were going to be any more producers like Star No. 1, the company was going to drill them. The California Star management offered in turn to buy Star No. 1 outright from Stewart and Hardison for cash. It looked like a hard bargain, but the partners had no other choice than to take it. Having no money either to develop this well or to drill, they sold out to get capital to start anew.

As it turned out, they didn't make such a bad deal. Some time later, when the California Star Oil Works Company pushed Star No. 1 down to 1,675 feet, the production fell to 35 barrels per day, one-half what it was when Hardison and Stewart sold. Furthermore, later drillings in the area proved that the well was on the extreme northern limit of production of the west side of a fault that extended down Pico Canyon. Had Hardison and Stewart drilled more wells on the lease, they might have gone broke right there.

The partners learned one important lesson from the Star No. 1 job, namely, that they should own the land on which they drilled good wells so they could sink more holes later without asking anybody's permission. They looked around for lands which they could buy with the money derived from the sale of Star No. 1. The broad valley of the Santa Clara River, which flowed through the little hamlet of Santa Paula, reminded them, except for its lack of forest, of the Venango Valley

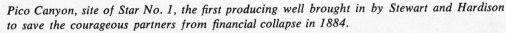

*Pico Canyon, site of Star No. 1, the first producing well brought in by Stewart and Hardison to save the courageous partners from financial collapse in 1884.*

54

in Pennsylvania, where they had had their first successes. Here there were hills similar to those along Pennsylvania's Oil Creek. Here there were oil seepages. Here they felt at home. With their Star No. 1 returns, they made the down payment on mineral rights to several thousand acres in Adams and Wheeler canyons and the Saltmarsh area back of Santa Paula. They also picked up mineral rights on several other small properties in Ventura County. What they lacked in capital they made up in daring.

Using as collateral the lands on which they had made down payment, they borrowed money right and left to get together a jackpot to drill again. They managed to drill an even dozen wells in 1884, but hard luck still plagued them. One of their best sites was Adams Canyon. Adams No. 1 came in for a small production. Encouraged, the partners spudded in Adams No. 2, 100 feet south of Adams No. 1. When No. 2 was put on the pump, it drained all the oil out of No. 1. Then they drilled No. 3 still farther south. It drained Adams No. 2 and made the first two wells unproductive. At this rate they were getting nowhere fast.

These Adams Canyon wells produced a heavy dead oil with a small kerosene content, which "smelled to high heaven." Gasoline was merely a by-product for which there was no demand, other than small amounts for cleaning fluids. Half of the oil, a heavy asphalt, was more or less a waste, although some of it was being used in limited quantities for saturating roofing paper, for coating iron pipes, and to surface roads.

At Ojai and on Smith Farm, the other wells they drilled were scarcely more promising. What small production the partners were able to pump, they delivered to a little refinery at Santa Paula, operated by E. A. Edwards, who had drilled a well in Adams Canyon in 1876 but shortly abandoned drilling to go into the refining business. In 1884 he bought 2,661 barrels of Hardison and Stewart's oil, all they produced that year. It was worth about $2.50 a barrel, and their income was far from enough to meet the expenses of one drilling crew, much less make any payments on their debts. They were kept alive by occasional dividends from oil leases back in Pennsylvania in which both men had small interests.

In 1884 one of their old Titusville associates, W. E. Youle, made a discovery that probably kept Stewart and Hardison from going broke completely. Youle had been employed by two promoters, W. R. Rowland and William Lacey, to drill some wells at Puente, not far from Los Angeles. There were tar seepages at Puente, and shallow wells drilled earlier had produced a heavy, almost useless oil at a 100-foot depth. Youle persuaded his backers to drill some distance away from the seepages. At 1,600 feet he got 150 barrels a day of oil suitable for fuel without refining. This was the first real proof that deep drilling paid in California.

*Adams Canyon in 1890 when the new-born Union Oil Company of California boasted a total of 26 wells and production of 84,421 barrels of crude for the entire year.*

*John Irwin, first field superintendent and first "geologist" employed by Union Oil Co.*

Hardison and Stewart visited Youle at the Puente field and they speculated on why he got more and better oil at deeper depths. They decided that the tar springs and the heavy oil from the shallow wells were by-products pushed up by pressures from larger oil deposits deeper down in the earth. The demonstration caused Stewart and Hardison to do some tall thinking about the geological formations along Adams Creek. They concluded that their new wells should be located by geological analysis of the faults, dips, and anticlines which could be traced from the outcroppings. They called in John Irwin, an experienced Pennsylvanian and a relative of Lyman Stewart, who was their first field superintendent.

"Go into Adams Canyon and see how deep drilling works out," they told him.

Irwin's crews drilled several deep wells, ranging down to nearly 3,000 feet, each producing from 5 to 300 barrels a day. There were some dry holes, but this Adams Canyon district was the first real oil production for Stewart and Hardison.

Eventually their idea paid off in California's first gusher, but in 1885 all they were able to produce was 4,806 barrels of oil.

Brooding over the cost of drilling, Lyman Stewart hit upon an idea that revolutionized not only the oil fields but industry throughout California. At the time it was the practice to use coal to fire the boilers that provided steam for the drilling-rig engine. It cost $30 a ton to deliver this coal to the oil fields. Stewart asked, "Why shouldn't we burn some of our own oil, just as it comes from the wells?" It had never been done. The first burners were kerosene burners that soon clogged with the heavy crude. Then Stewart had the crews try dripping the oil on a bed of rocks. Later they blew it into the firebox in a spray. Eventually, the shop mechanics came up with a nozzle that did the trick, when properly placed in the firebox. All the oil-field rigs were quickly switched over to oil burners. Lyman Stewart became the crusading apostle of oil fuel throughout California. His gospel more than doubled the potential market for California crude.

Stewart and Hardison had laid small pipelines to deliver their crude from their wells to the little refinery at Santa Paula. But that failed to solve the bigger problem of getting their oil to market. Refinery products had to be pumped into tank cars or into barrels and hauled by rail to Los Angeles and to San Francisco, the latter being the larger market. It cost a dollar a barrel to ship the oil by rail to the San Francisco area. When the Southern Pacific refused to lower rates, the partners decided to build a pipeline from the oil fields to tidewater. Putting C. A. Burrows,

56

a brother-in-law of Lyman Stewart, in charge, early in 1886 they launched a stupendous undertaking for two wildcatters already hard pressed by their creditors. Undaunted, they brought 4-inch pipeline around the Horn to Ventura and San Pedro and hauled it by wagon to the mountainous country, cut by deep canyons and barrancas, over which the pipeline was suspended by cables. It was back-breaking labor, but by the end of the year the line was completed. Hardison and Stewart oil flowed 40 miles from Newhall down to Ventura, where it was put in barrels and shipped by water at less than half the rail rate to San Francisco. That year they were able to increase their production to 35,355 barrels, roughly one-tenth of the California output.

Moving from the tiny room in Newhall to the growing and thriving town of Santa Paula, farther down the valley, they now established headquarters in a one-story frame building. Santa Paula was but a frontier agricultural community into which a number of unwelcome wild-west gun-toting characters had moved in the wake of the oil strike. The latter were not only heavy drinkers but quick shooters, who terrorized the 200 inhabitants. Santa Paula boasted the dubious distinction of having a saloon for every seven families. One saloon, directly across the street from the Hardison & Stewart headquarters, pained Lyman Stewart especially, because the drilling crews when they came to town drew their pay and made a bee-line for it. After watching them come out on anything but a beeline, Stewart persuaded Hardison that they should put up a new office building on Main Street on a

*C. A. Burrows in 1886 laid world's first oil pipeline from producing fields to the sea.*

site which faced no saloon. Soon after they finished the building, an enterprising tavernkeeper placed a brace of swinging doors directly across Main Street.

The Stewarts and the Hardisons, no small addition to the community, populationwise, plunged into the task of making rough Santa Paula a good place for family life, just as they and their kith and kin had transformed Titusville from a rip-roaring oil-boom town into a sedate and cultured little city. The Stewarts consisted of Lyman, his wife, Sarah Adelaide Burrows, sons Alfred C. and William Lyman, daughters May and Eva, plus various relations who had joined them in the Western trek. Wallace Hardison had a son, Guy, two daughters, Augusta and Hope, and soon after the firm was established various of his brothers and their families came West. Though the youngest of 11 children, Wallace L. Hardison was the dynamic leader of the clan. A stocky, rugged, robust 200-pounder with springy step, black mustache and hair, Hardison was an outdoor man who loved horses,

57

politics, and farming. A born promoter, he immediately began converting the semi-desert around the little town into one of California's richest agricultural areas, renowned for its citrus and walnut crops.

Lyman Stewart's interests were more concentrated. They were oil, his family, and the Presbyterian Church. A smallish, slender man of great dignity, immaculate even out in the oil fields, Stewart with his carefully trimmed beard was an incongruous figure among the rough, swearing drilling crews. Stewart worried about his drillers, their swearing, chewing, and drinking, and their unsaved souls, yet the men liked him and drove themselves under his prodding. One of his first acts in building up Santa Paula as a community was to raise money for a Presbyterian church.

Hardison, though not a zealot like his partner, was a religious man, too, helping to organize the Santa Paula Universalist Church, to which he gave liberally. Before long the Stewarts and the Hardisons were competing in stained-glass windows, in visiting preachers, and in bringing culture, in the form of music, lectures, and readings, to Santa Paula. It was the first sign of rivalry in the rare business relationship between Wallace Hardison and Lyman Stewart who, though they were trusting partners with unlimited faith in each other, were never close friends. After two decades of bonanza and vicissitude, they were still "Mr. Stewart" and "Mr. Hardison" to each other. Hardison's interest in the company decreased in proportion to its success and he turned to new enterprises; Stewart's enthusiasm grew apace with the business.

Up to 1883 Hardison and Stewart was an informal and purely verbal partnership. With the prospect of greatly expanded operation in the West, they decided to draw up a written partnership, in which Lyman Stewart and his family owned 51 per cent, Hardison and his friends 49 per cent. Stewart was already head of Lyman Stewart & Company, a family partnership

*Mission Transfer Company, a marketing and transportation subsidiary of Union Oil, was housed in this tiny one-story frame structure at Santa Paula about 1886.*

which included two brothers and two sisters, plus John Irwin, his cousin, and W. J. Chichester, a Presbyterian minister. Alexander Waldie also owned 1 per cent. Spasmodic income from this family partnership kept the Lyman Stewart family in food and clothing during the lean early years in California.

Desperately needing money and thinking that the formal partnership made them better prospects for a loan, Lyman Stewart journeyed to Los Angeles to talk I. W. Hellman, the town's leading banker, out of another $30,000. Stewart and Hardison already owed Hellman several thousand. Hellman explained that business was business and that their position was not particularly strong. He was sorry, but he couldn't let them have the $30,000. But before Stewart left the office, he changed his mind, at least to the extent of asking for a statement in full of the Hardison-Stewart affairs. The thought of drawing up a statement made Lyman Stewart shudder, but he got it together and submitted it.

"Well, I didn't sleep any that night, I can tell you," Stewart recalled later. "Hellman called me into his office the next day. As I entered, he was holding the statement in his hand, and didn't speak for what seemed a long time, although it was only a minute, I guess. He shook his head, and then said, 'Stewart, this doesn't look as good as I'd like it to, but draw checks for $10,000 and I'll sign them.'"

That $10,000 tided them over one crisis. A short time later the partners got some unexpected dividends from oil wells back in Pennsylvania in which they still had minor interests. That saved another day. They decided that to make a real success of the oil business in California they would have to go after big money. The richest man in the county was Thomas R. Bard, the same Bard who had come out for Colonel Tom Scott to drill the wells on the vast ranch acreage which Scott and his friends had bought as a result of the enthusiastic report of Professor Silliman. When drilling failed to produce oil in any quantity, Bard had turned to buying up distressed properties for the Scott syndicate. This had proved highly profitable, and Bard himself was already a millionaire. His only oil interest was the little company known as the Mission Transfer Company which owned several thousand acres of land in the Rancho Ex-Mission de San Buena Ventura, tanks, pipelines, and a small refinery, and did a thriving business transporting and marketing other producers' oil.

Bard had sold a one-half interest in the Mission Transfer Company to the Pacific Coast Oil Company, the big competitor of Hardison and Stewart. Much to their surprise, he agreed to sell the other half to them. He also was quite receptive to the idea of launching a new oil company to drill in Sespe Canyon on proved oil lands which Hardison and Stewart controlled through leases. Thus in 1886 the Sespe Oil Company came into existence with Bard as president and "angel," although Hardison and Stewart got the majority of the stock in exchange for their leases. Dan McFarland of Los Angeles, a well-to-do friend of Bard, owned one-fifth of Sespe. Soon after this deal was consummated, Hardison and Stewart bought the other half of the Mission Transfer Company from the Pacific Coast Oil Company. Bard also served as president of Mission Transfer, although the control and management were entirely in the hands of the Hardison and Stewart partnership.

On December 28, 1886, the Hardison and Stewart partnership was terminated. The partners concluded they were getting into such involved financing that it would be better handled by a corporation. So the Hardison & Stewart Oil Company was incorporated, with a capital of 1 million dollars, consisting of 10,000 shares

of a $100 par value each. Lyman Stewart was president, Hardison vice-president and general manager, and the other incorporators included Thomas R. Bard, Dan McFarland, Walter H. Chaffee, Alexander Waldie, John Irwin, I. H. Warring, and Casper Taylor, all personalities who were to figure prominently in the spectacular feuds for the control of an oil empire.

By 1887, four years after they started hopefully to drill their way to riches, Lyman Stewart and Wallace Hardison were still getting too little oil to meet their overhead, much less make payments on their debt. That year they branched

*Star Lease of Union Oil at mouth of the Big Sespe in Ventura County in 1890.*

out and drilled in Tar Canyon, an off-shoot of the Little Sespe, getting a little better production, but still not enough. In fact, the situation became so desperate that by the end of the year they were forced to sell mules, boilers, engines, and miscellaneous equipment to meet the more pressing demands for money. But they managed to bring their production up to 50,000 barrels that year, approximately one-seventh of the entire California output.

Desperately in need of money, Stewart dropped his work in the field, where he was continually prodding his crews to more production, to plead with I. W.

Hellman, the Los Angeles banker, for more money. This time Hellman was adamant. Hardison and Stewart already owed him $40,000. When the banker turned a deaf ear to his plea, Stewart was at the end of his rope. But in the nick of time, Hardison managed to raise several thousand dollars from Eastern sources. "It is another providential deliverance," Stewart wrote when Hardison reported about the money he had borrowed. Yet Stewart found time to carry on a $14,500 drive to raise money for the Y.M.C.A. in Santa Paula.

It was a year to try men's mettle. Eastern competitors were coming into the Los

*Tar Creek in Ventura County in 1890 had some of Union Oil's best producers.*

Angeles and San Francisco markets with a better, clearer, and less odorous illuminating oil with which they undersold the California oil refineries. Kerosene was the profitable end of the business. Although they were barely able to keep their heads above the financial waters, Hardison and Stewart decided, with characteristic brashness, to build at Santa Paula a new refinery which they hoped would produce a better illuminant. The refinery had a capacity of 14,000 barrels a year.

By 1888 it looked as though luck had changed for the better for the partners. In January Adams Canyon Well No. 16 came in with a roar. Their good fortune is revealed by their log, which reads:

"Adams Canyon Well No. 16, which was completed in January at a depth of 750 feet, is the largest flowing well ever struck in California. The oil shot up to a height of nearly 100 feet, and flowed at the rate of 800 to 900 barrels a day. Before it could be controlled, it sent a stream down the canyon for a distance of 7 miles. After a lapse of nine months, it continues to flow at the rate of 500 barrels daily. At the present time it is producing sufficient gas to run all the works and machinery in the canyon."

Their first gusher, and California's as well, partially compensated for some of the more dismal entries in the Adams' Canyon logbook, such as these:

"Adams Canyon No. 23. At 1,580 feet we drilled for four days on iron which was put in the hole by someone."

"Adams No. 35. Drilled the well to

50 feet and shot for a crooked hole. Too much explosive and wrecked the derrick badly."

"Salt Marsh No. 6. Dry as dust."

Even with all the oil from California's first gusher flowing into their refinery and on to the markets, Hardison and Stewart were still on the verge of financial collapse. Bankers all over the state were cracking down on them. In San Francisco the Wells Fargo Bank demanded settlement on notes, saying "We expect immediate payment." The Santa Barbara National Bank turned Hardison down cold on a loan. At the Hellman bank a check for $5,000 was protested because of lack of funds, and at the Farmers and Mechanics Bank in Los Angeles several small checks bounced. Alexander Waldie, secretary of the company, warned Hardison that the "Mission Transfer's balance at this moment is between $500 and $600, and the amounts coming in may not be here in time to take up our notes for $5,429.75, which mature Monday next."

Back in Pennsylvania, Milton Stewart was turned down on a loan and was having his own troubles, and complained to Hardison and Stewart that he had already "advanced over and above my assessment, $4,500, on which I think there should be some adjustment." Even Bard was using up all his connections and influence to raise dollars to keep the company afloat. Sales were good, and the partners figured that if they could only tide themselves over the immediate emergencies they could survive.

Lyman Stewart's personal finances were in even worse shape than those of

62

*Santa Paula in 1950 as seen from the still-productive South Mountain Field.*

the company. From his sickbed he wrote to the treasurer of Hardison & Stewart Oil Company, on October 7, 1888, asking if they could spare $200 or $300 to enable him to meet his more pressing demands. The company treasurer was able to spare only 100 dollars. A week or so later Stewart was still pleading for a couple of hundred dollars. "Sometimes I think I am engaged in a losing battle," he wrote. "During the past three weeks I have probably lost 20 pounds of my surplus flesh—well, hardly of the surplus, for I didn't have that amount."

While lying on his sickbed, Stewart had plenty of time to think, not only about debt and money shortages but overhead in general. One of the biggest expenses was still tank-car rates to San Francisco, their main market. It still cost $1 to ship a barrel of oil to most California markets. The railroad adamantly refused to cut rates. Stewart called in Hardison and Bard. He outlined a scheme to take their oil from their pipeline at tidewater and deliver it to the San Francisco market for less. All agreed that Stewart had the solution to much of their financial problems, if they could only raise the money to try it. Without delay, they drew up plans for a wooden schooner, a steamer with sail auxiliary to have a capacity of

63

*Thomas R. Bard, first president of Union Oil, served October 17, 1890 to July 24, 1894.*

*Wallace L. Hardison, the co-founder of Union Oil of California and its first treasurer.*

around 6,500 barrels in a series of steel tanks. Somehow they scraped together the money. Before the year ended, the "W. L. Hardison" was launched and ready for trial runs.

Then they ran into a new difficulty. Because of a series of accidents on smaller craft using oil fuel, the steamboat inspector of San Francisco refused a certificate to steamers using oil as fuel. Lyman Stewart was equally determined that the "Hardison" should burn oil. Bard, who

was influential politically, finally used this weight with officials in Washington to overrule the inspector. They secured a temporary permit and proved that oil made a safe, good, and less expensive fuel for steamers. It was a revolutionary step, one that launched Lyman Stewart on a tremendous crusade to switch practically all the Pacific Coast shipping over to oil burners.

The "W. L. Hardison" did what it was expected to do. As soon as it began oper-

*First tank steamer on the Pacific ablaze at Ventura, California. The "W. L. Hardison" was built for Hardison & Stewart Oil Co. late in 1888 and destroyed in July, 1889. So precarious were firm's finances a second tanker could not be built for 11 years.*

ating, the rail rates dropped from $1 to 50 cents a barrel; and just in time, too, for shortly after midnight on June 25, 1889, a Chinese cook spilled a pan of burning fat in the galley of the "W. L. Hardison" as it was moored along the wharf at Ventura. Fanned by breezes, the blaze spread. The ship was cut adrift. By morning the fire had burned out the hulk, and the first tanker on the Pacific was a total loss. Hardison and Stewart had no money to build another. It was eleven years before they were able to own a second tanker, the "Santa Paula."

Despite their financial pains, known mainly to insiders, the Hardison & Stewart Oil Company looked good to outsiders. On December 31, 1888, the company's achievements were summed up by the *Los Angeles Times* in a story which read:

"The Hardison & Stewart Oil Company is now actively engaged in developing their interests up in Ventura County. During the past year several new and productive wells have been drilled, and production is up to 236,703 barrels, as against 121,355 barrels for 1887. The following shipments have been made: Los Angeles, 71,775 barrels; San Francisco, 119,706 barrels; San Diego, 17,-491 barrels. During the past year the company has erected expensive refining works at Santa Paula, in which about 14,000 barrels have been manufactured into gas, oil, lubricants; machine, wool, illuminating oils; asphaltum, and so forth.

"The company has large tanks at Hueneme, Santa Paula, Ventura, San Diego, and San Francisco. It has 90 miles of pipeline connecting the various oil tanks of the county. It also has 60 miles

of telephone wires in operation. It has built 52 oil tank cars, and an expensive $40,000 steamer with a capacity of 6,500 barrels is about completed and will receive her cargoes of oil at Hueneme. The writer believes that the oil interests of this county (Ventura) are in their infancy and that the near future will develop untold wealth in this direction."

The constant expansion and debt, which failed to dampen the enthusiasm of perpetual optimists like Hardison and Stewart, was anything but good medicine for their new associate, Thomas R. Bard, vice-president of three of the other companies, the third being the Torrey Canyon Oil Company. The conservative Bard advocated curtailment, even to the point of closing the refinery. Differences of opinion increased month by month until Bard and Stewart were at opposite ends of the pole on company policies. Stewart was always on the lookout for a new oil lease, continuously experimenting with new products for new markets. Stewart considered the refinery the key to the oil business. He argued that only by refining an illuminant as good as that produced from Pennsylvania crude could the Western oil producers compete on equal terms with their Eastern rivals. Until they had a good kerosene, the market for California's oil industry would be limited to the low-priced products, fuel oil, asphaltum, greases, and lubricants.

Still beset by ill health which kept him confined to his bed for extended periods, Stewart fought doggedly to keep the companies afloat. Though demands for oil products were picking up with the increase in population in California, the output from their wells was decreasing. New wells failed to keep pace with the demand. On Christmas Day of 1888 Stewart, still ill, took time off from the family festivities to write to Hardison about a scheme for producing more oil, namely, to dig deep tunnels into Sulphur Mountain, the mountain of oil sands tapped in the early sixties by Josiah Stanford. Tunnels would produce oil cheaper.

Hardison by this time had branched out into agriculture and was one of the state's leading citrus growers. He was also being urged by influential politicians to accept the nomination for state senator. Although tempted by the offer, he turned it down and again tackled the job of raising more money for the Hardison and Stewart Oil Company. While Hardison hunted money, Stewart, when he was able to get up from his sickbed, was out in the fields, driving the oil crews harder than ever. In spite of this financial distress, the company was growing. On June 10, 1889, Hardison recapitulated in a letter to Honorable F. G. Babcock of Hornellsville, New York:

"Our oil business has grown very rapidly. We now have a very large scope of territory, have over 100 miles of pipeline with terminal facilities at Hueneme, San Buena Ventura, and San Francisco, and have a finely equipped refinery at Santa Paula. We have 54 new tank cars, each with a capacity of 3,800 gallons, and have a new steamer designed especially for carrying oil in bulk. We have our own teams and supplies. In fact, we have the best equipped arrangement for producing and marketing oil that I know of, not excepting the Standard Oil Company. The oil business in this state is peculiar. We have worked up an excellent market, but are unable at the present time to supply the demand at handsome prices. We hope, however, in the near future to have more territory developed and be able to supply the increasing demands. We are now getting for our oil $2 and $2.25, delivered at San Francisco and Los Angeles. The cost of delivery to Los Angeles is about 30 cents a barrel, and to San Francisco, when our steamer runs steadily, the cost will probably not exceed 12 to 15 cents per barrel."

By December, 1889, after almost seven years of hunting oil under California's canyons and hills, Lyman Stewart and Wallace Hardison were still broke. In a letter remarkable for its restraint under the existing conditions, December 7, 1889, Stewart wrote to Hardison: "I saw Mr. Bixby today and he wants some money from me on account of what I owe him, in time to use it in payment of his taxes. Can you help me out to the extent of $750? I am not very well; my head has given out again."

But Stewart's fighting heart hadn't given out, and in spite of their financial difficulties, by now well known to almost everybody, he and Hardison were highly respected as businessmen. Eastern interests had been watching the growing California company. Just before Christmas in 1889, Stewart and Hardison received an offer from an Eastern syndicate to buy 49 per cent of the three companies they controlled, namely, the Hardison & Stewart Oil Company (which owned the Mission Transfer Company outright), the Sespe Oil Company, and the Torrey Canyon Oil Company. In consideration for a substantial share in a new refining process developed by Dr. Frederick Salathe, a distinguished Swiss chemist, they accepted, granting an option on 49 per cent of the stock they held to Daniel Dull of New York and Ambrose C. Burdick of Chicago. Dull and Burdick promised that their new process would double the amount of water-white kerosene extracted from California crude. If successful, it would revolutionize the West's oil business.

A part of the deal was that the three companies must be merged into one large corporation, which would own all the properties, including the Mission Transfer Company and its marketing facilities. On Christmas Day, 1889, Lyman Stewart ordered an appraisal of all their properties, preparatory to closing the deal with the Easterners. Not only Hardison and Stewart, but others as well, were amazed at the value of the business which had grown from their borrowed shoestring. The properties were appraised at $1,800,000, although the companies were all fresh out of cash, as usual. Though Dull and Burdick never exercised their option, probably because the claims for their process proved extravagant and they were unable to live up to their part of the bargain, Stewart, Hardison, and Bard decided to merge the three companies anyway, with Thomas R. Bard as president, Lyman Stewart as vice-president, W. L. Hardison as treasurer, I. H. Warring, secretary; John Irwin, Alexander Waldie, Dan McFarland, W. S. Chaffee, and Casper Taylor as directors.

Thus, on October 17, 1890, the borrowed shoestring became the Union Oil Company of California.

# CHAPTER FIVE

# Wildcatters' Paradise

IN the decade following the timely birth of the Union Oil Company in 1890, California blossomed into a wildcatters' paradise. Where the Newhall-Ventura field had been the only area in which a prospector could punch a hole with hope of quick riches, after the Humboldt and Santa Cruz pools ran dry, vast chains of pools and even lakes of petroleum appeared to be hidden under the state's valleys, deserts, and hills. There were oceans of oil, some of it actually under the Pacific, waiting for men to come and get it.

What brought about this new conception of the potential Black Bonanza hidden beneath California's precipitous, forbidding slopes and numerous deep basins was W. E. Youle's pioneer "deep" well at Puente, yielding 150 barrels a day, the state's first real producer. Acting on that tip-off, Stewart and Hardison instructed John Irwin, their superintendent in Adams Canyon, to drill deeper. The hunch paid off. Adams No. 16 came in

for 800 barrels a day and made oil history.

Came Adams No. 28 in February, 1892, with a whooshing roar that sent oil bursting over the derrick. It was the state's biggest gusher, flowing 1,500 barrels a day. Catching the drenched drillers by surprise, the oil poured over the top, filled the tanks and sumps, flowed down the canyon to the Santa Clara River to the open sea. Here was the river of oil Professor Silliman had predicted a quarter century before. Irwin and his crew frantically dammed up ravines to catch the oil in reservoirs. Adams No. 28 spewed 40,000 barrels of crude out of the bowels of the earth before settling down to a steady 200 barrels a day.

This was the kind of oil strike men dreamed of and risked their all to get. It faded all other drilling jobs up to that time in California and changed the whole oil outlook, multiplying the state's potential a hundredfold. It touched off a new oil stampede, as hectic and reckless in the eager struggle for quick riches as Pennsylvania's oil boom had been in the sixties, or the California Gold Rush in the fifties. This time, prospectors were combing the state for liquid black gold, battling not only nature but each other for fortune. Hundreds found it. Thousands lost it. Such was the Black Bonanza.

In this relentless scramble to tap the deep-down pools of oil, Union crews drilled furiously, prodded by the prim and unexcitable little man with the neatly trimmed goatee. Though they never understood him, the rough and blasphemous drillers in the baggy, grimy overalls liked and respected Lyman Stewart. They put up derricks and made hole faster because he asked them in gentleman's language to do it.

Though no geologist, Lyman Stewart was one of the first to sense the scope of the oil pools that nature in the course of millions of years had hidden under the state. A sixth sense or a nose for oil enabled him to smell potential oil where there was no sign of it. Stewart picked up acreages as most men pick out neckties, shrewdly sensing that the day of cheap land, $2 to $10 an acre, would soon pass.

*Side of cliff is cut away to make site for Moran No. 1, a Union well in Ventura County, California. Note difference in angles of formation at left and right of derrick.*

*This lonely well drilled by Union Oil in seeking to extend its Poso Creek Field in 1950 was abandoned at 5,204 feet as a "duster." Company's closest producing well is nearly a mile away.*

He bought it on his own hunch, then told his associates in Union about it after he had already committed them. His buying and leasing kept the struggling company on the brink of bankruptcy, with the hot breath of the bankers on the officers' necks continuously. But Lyman Stewart's mania for more and more acreage provided his drillers with the land on which to put up their derricks and sink their holes for many decades to come. Their early battles to make hole to the deep pools they suspected were down there, without knowing exactly where, are an important chapter in the saga of oil.

If one kind of hole wouldn't get the oil, another one would. The ingenuity of the early field crews was dramatized in the Adams Canyon oil hunt. Adams No. 16 and Adams No. 28 were outstanding examples of holes drilled deeper. Adams No. 3 and a score of other Adams numbers were something else again. They were holes tunneled into the side of Sulphur Mountain, forming one of the canyon's walls. Sulphur Mountain was too precipitous a peak on which to perch a derrick and enginehouse. Yet the earlier tunnels of Josiah Stanford had proved there was a huge deposit of oil-bearing sand inside the mountain, oil that would trickle out into tanks if holes were pushed into the cliffs near the base, with the mouths lower than the inner ends.

Adams Tunnel No. 3 was known as "The Boarding House Tunnel" in the

71

*Frank Hill invented the oil-well cementing process while Union's field superintendent.*

inexplicable vernacular of oil-field crews. Harvey Hardison, brother of Wallace, was the boss on the job. By April 4, 1890, The Boarding House was 950 feet deep. Early that morning, an explosion deep in the hole shook the mountain. Two men at the mouth were slightly burned; two more inside were more seriously injured. Wallace Hardison, arriving on the scene, ordered the workers to stay out of the tunnel after the injured men were rescued. While he was taking them to the hospital, Harvey Hardison and three workers decided to make an inspection. When they were 700 feet inside, another explosion rocked

the mountain, killing Hardison and two other men. Despite the tragedy, Union's crews finished The Boarding House and 30 other tunnels, some 1,600 feet long. One was still trickling oil commercially half a century later. The price of oil was blood, as well as sweat and toil and dollars.

These were rough and ready, gun-toting days of the California oil industry. The lands under which much of the west-side San Joaquin Valley oil lay were originally classified as mineral lands. In 1896 the Secretary of the Interior reversed the rulings of his predecessors and decreed that the lands were not mineral but were homestead lands. There was a rush of homesteaders to the area, although it was barren and unsuited to agriculture. Soon there were conflicting claims between prospectors who had filed on mineral lands and the homesteaders. Unwilling to wait for the courts tediously to decide the ownership, both sides got out their guns to protect their rights. Drilling crews often found that they were putting down wells in no man's land, as was illustrated when one of Union's crews, headed by Frank Hill, later production superintendent for the company, undertook to wildcat a lease on the west side of the San Joaquin Valley.

"We had a drilling deal at Maricopa to put in wells on each half-section of a lease," recalls Hill. "I took my crew

*Mixing cement preparatory to plugging Hellman 53, well in Dominguez Field. By using cement behind the casing, water-bearing sands are shut off, leaving open only those strata that yield oil.*

*Readily portable drilling mast can be used, dismounted, erected again for another well.*

up there, and as we stepped on the lease we were met by a group of gunmen who leveled rifles at us. They told us to get the hell out of there, and get out fast. One of them I recognized as a Los Angeles Superior Court judge. He had waving white whiskers, but his gun didn't waver a bit. We tried to tell them we had a legal lease, but they said the people who had given us the lease had no right to the land and that the land belonged to them. Well, we were drillers and certainly not in a mood to do any gun fighting. So we got the hell out, like they said. We later drilled there, but that was after our land boys leased it from the gunmen who ran us off. That judge used his gun as well as his lawbook, and it was plenty effective."

Oil fields were blossoming all over the upper San Joaquin Valley. On the heels of the Coalinga boom came the discovery of the McKittrick field in 1898 and the Midway Sunset field in 1900. Across the valley east of Bakersfield, the Kern River field burst into production in 1900. Then came the discovery in the Santa Maria and Lompoc fields in Santa Barbara County. In all these new fields, Lyman Stewart was busily lining up land. Having missed the parade in the fantastic, booming Los Angeles City field, he made up for his losses particularly in the Santa Maria, Lompoc, and San Joaquin areas.

In the Lompoc Valley, Union's oil hunters concluded that the geologic features were such as to indicate the possibility of an American Baku, the prodigiously rich Russian field. Lyman Stewart rounded up options on lands until Union's holdings in this area totaled 72,000 acres, most of them valued at grazing-land prices. The surface or agricultural rights to the land could be resold and the oil and mineral rights retained. Usually the purchase took the form of an option, which gave the company just enough time to sink test wells. This inevitably meant a race against the deadline. The company's wildcatters drilled like mad to prove up the Lompoc land before the option expired. Frank Hill, whose crew brought in the discovery well in the Lompoc field, describes the excitement of these battles of men against nature.

"We were drilling Hill No. 1, a wildcat in the Purissima hills near Lompoc, to test the territory there, where we had 72,000 acres under option until December 1, 1902. We had to race against time, because the option was a short one. I was in charge of the wildcatting. In those days, crews worked on twelve-hour tours. Owing to the importance of this well, we kept three tool dressers on the job to meet any emergency. We had only two drillers, but every few hours I took a turn on the rig, giving the drillers a breather.

"We landed in Lompoc the night of

*Moving 129-foot portable single-unit steel derrick from one Union Oil field to another saves many days. The derrick shown measured 30 feet 9 inches at the base and weighed 23 tons.*

*Boiler plant ready for drilling operations in one of the arid sections of California's vast San Joaquin valley. Sometimes water for the boilers, to make "mud" and quench the thirst of the crew, in early days approached oil in value per barrel, if it had to be hauled many miles.*

July 14, 1902, with our steam cable drilling rig. By the next day the well location was made and the road grades were staked out. We bought lumber locally and knocked together a bunkhouse. We put up the tanks and built the derrick. Water was a problem. We located and cleaned out two springs. We weren't wasting a minute—we didn't have any minutes to spare, because the option expiration date was just around the corner. Seventeen days after we hit the field, we had spudded in our first well.

"Everyone was on his toes, because this was a race we could win only if we all pitched in, and nothing serious happened. Then it did happen. Some dumb-bell had shipped us a string of casing in which 13 joints of secondhand stuff had no coupling. The air was pretty blue for a while. There wasn't anything to do but yell for more pipe and couplings. We couldn't put down a foot more of hole, because by this time the hole was caving and we couldn't drill without casing.

"Finally the new casing arrived. We drove ourselves day and night. Shift hours were forgotten in the excitement of the race. Saturday night on most drilling jobs then was pretty much a letdown time after a week of hard work. This last Saturday night, no one left the rig. A little after dark we struck oil. We had won by three days."

76

The land had oil, all right. Hill tried to keep it secret, knowing Lyman Stewart didn't want anyone else to know what his drillers had hit. Around midnight, Hill caught a train for Los Angeles to report. Putting on an act, he climbed aboard with dragging footsteps. Frank Garbutt, one of the company's directors, met him the next morning with his brand new 1902 merry Oldsmobile. They chugged off to Sixth and Lucas streets where Lyman Stewart lived. Just as they reached the house, Stewart came out of the door with his Bible under his arm. They knew he never talked or did business on the Sabbath. Seeing Garbutt and Hill, Stewart knew something was up. He shifted from one foot to the other. They did the same. Nobody mentioned the oil well. He wanted to know and they wanted to tell him, but here it was, Sunday, and business was taboo. Finally, Lyman Stewart asked guardedly, "What have you got?"

"We've got us an oil well."

"What does it look like?"

"Pretty heavy," said Hill, taking a bottle out of his pocket. "Here is a sample." Stewart stuck his finger in and rubbed the smelly stuff back and forth between a finger and a thumb. Finally he said:

"We'll take up the option tomorrow. This is Sunday—had you forgotten?"

Not another word was spoken. Stewart continued down the street to the church, acting as if he had expected oil all the time but still knew nothing about it.

Stewart's dogmatic insistence that all work be suspended over the Sabbath often interfered seriously with field operations. Oil wells had a devilish habit of coming in on Saturday night, as did the Lompoc discovery job. Lyman Stewart finally relented to the extent of agreeing to a resolution of the board of directors that field superintendents might decide whether halting work arbitrarily would seriously affect the life of the well. After that, Union's field bosses interpreted the new instructions quite liberally—without reporting their decisions to headquarters.

Lyman Stewart worried about his drillers and prayed for their oil-blackened, unsaved souls. To keep them humping, he dropped in on field jobs when he was least expected. The talk he heard sometimes knocked his eardrums loose. One incident finally galvanized him to action. Arriving unannounced on a wildcat drilling job in the Torrey Canyon field, he

*"Don't ask the depth of the other fellow's well and never tell him depth of your own."*

found the drillers stretched out in the shade asleep while a sweating boy pumped a bellows nearby. The youngster was obviously tired. Lyman Stewart walked over to him, glanced at the sleeping men, then said sympathetically,

"Well, son, that is pretty heavy work for a fellow your size, isn't it?"

"Mister, she is a --- -- - ----- and you can tell the whole --- ---- world I said so," the boy replied, adding his opinion of the sleeping men in sizzling oil-field lingo.

Horrified at the lad's language, Stewart backed out of earshot. At the next meeting of Union's directors, he got authorization to build a chapel in Torrey Canyon and to employ the Reverend Mr. Johnson to conduct services in it. A little later he induced them to vote that "a temperance rendezvous be built to contain a temperance bar, a library, a reading room, a gymnasium, and so forth for the purpose of giving men and boys a place to spend their evenings and keeping them out of saloons."

Unfortunately — or fortunately — this burning urge to save the souls of the employees was not shared by Lyman Stewart's son William, who learned the oil game the hard way, emerging as a rough and ready field superintendent. Lyman Stewart could never quite reconcile himself to Will Stewart's tolerance. The contrasting viewpoints between father and son became more apparent as the

*Massive boiler plant in the Rio Bravo field northwest of Bakersfield. Hanging from the derrick are drilling pipe and tubing made into 90-foot lengths to facilitate handling.*

78

years went on. Lyman became more devout as Will grew more tolerant. One day Lyman Stewart told Will to fire a drilling foreman who reportedly showed up on the job sober but gradually got drunk.

"No man who starts to work sober and ends up half drunk should be retained on Union's payroll," Lyman contended.

Will Stewart replied that he knew the man well; he was a hard-working and dependable employee. Will said emphatically that any report that the man showed up sober and ended up drunk was false. Pleased to have this assurance from his son, Lyman Stewart relented. Will Stewart afterward explained, but not to his father, that the man was a good driller, and "whoever reported him as starting out sober and getting drunk on the job was a liar, because the man never does show up sober. He is always half drunk when he starts to work."

When unable to lease or buy land, Lyman Stewart often got the oil by lending a rig or a driller to an independent operator. This made many friends for the company among the independents. It also gave the crews drilling on Union leases something to shoot at, because the independents were notoriously fast at making hole. How fast it was possible to bang down a well into the earth was demonstrated by Jack Reed, for forty-five years a Union Oil driller, who was once loaned to a small operator short of help.

*Noiseless drilling makes for more friendly neighbors, so Union Oil put this dress of fire-resistant fabric padded with glass wool around Sansinena well near Whittier.*

79

"We really made hole with that cable outfit," Reed recalled. "The driller I was working with then knew his stuff. I was young and hated to see him do more than I did. Besides, I felt the prestige of the company was at stake. So between us we dug 5,000 feet in just forty-two days— that was a record. I showed that fellow he couldn't make hole faster than I could. It was real competition. Then I found out why—the fellow was the owner of the well, and the faster he worked, the faster I did. Anyway, we set a record for drillers to shoot at for a good many years to come."

Only once, so far as the records reveal, did Lyman Stewart try wildcatting on the side. This was in 1888, when he and Dan McFarland took a flyer on a well near the Hancock brea pits, later famous as the source of relics of prehistoric animals. These pits were some distance west of Los Angeles. Later an oil field was developed here, but when Stewart and McFarland drilled their wildcat hole alongside what seemed to be a sure-fire oil field, because the tar was seeping to the surface, they came up with a duster.

As a result, Union backed out of the Los Angeles area—too soon. It was one

of the few instances in which Stewart's nose for oil failed him. In April, 1893, Edward L. Doheny, with a pick and shovel, dug a wildcat hole, a shaft 4 by 6 feet, on a lot just west of downtown Los Angeles. At a depth of 460 feet he dipped up 4 barrels of oil a day. This unusual hand-dug discovery well touched off the hectic Los Angeles City oil scramble. Not only Doheny but everybody who could scrape together a few hundred dollars to buy or lease a lot began digging or punching oil wells. They were shallow, cheap wells, the average cost being under $1,500, including tanks and pumps. A good many of them were put down by the spring-pole method. By 1899 there were more than three thousand wells in the narrow tract of land varying from 1,500 to 800 feet wide and about 4½ miles long.

The drilling became so frantic that the City Council was forced to declare oil wells a civic nuisance and to clamp down on oil-well drilling within the city limits. Suddenly, everybody who had a lot on the west side of town discovered that he needed water badly and right away. The city fathers couldn't very well forbid citizens from drilling wells for water to keep their gardens green. If the water well happened to produce oil instead of water, that was just lucky. The drillers drilled so exuberantly that an ocean of oil flooded the Los Angeles market and ruined it. This hit the company where it

hurt, because Los Angeles was Union's No. 2 market.

Belatedly, Lyman Stewart decided to go into the area, although his Scotch blood curdled at the thought of paying city prices for lots on which to drill, as much as $1,500 for a 25-foot lot. By the time he had three producing wells in the Los Angeles field, the bottom dropped out of oil. It was cheaper to buy oil already pumped than to pump Union's wells. Soon the Los Angeles City fields tapered off and almost petered out. The oil scramble shifted to the new San Joaquin Valley fields, then to the Lompoc and Santa Maria valleys. Ironically, neither Lyman Stewart nor the eager drillers who moved their rigs out of the Los Angeles area and north over the mountains knew that they were leaving behind them the greatest untapped lake of oil in California. This was the Greater Los Angeles Basin, covering an area 22 miles long and 46 miles wide, south and west of the city and extending under the ocean, a small area from which another generation of oil hunters were to pump 3.5 billion barrels of oil from deeper wells than the drillers of that day ever dreamed of sinking.

Before they could get at the ocean of oil in the deep pools, not only in the fabulous Los Angeles Basin but elsewhere in California as well, Union's drillers and their rivals working for other companies had to learn the hard way how to drill deeper holes. They also had to

*Cat Canyon, southeast of Orcutt, California, was part of the 4,000-acre Bell estate in Santa Barbara County purchased in 1907 by Union Oil. Field is still a good producer.*

81

*Many lengths of heavy drill pipe are used in driving oil well miles into the rocky earth.*

unlock the secrets of California's jumbled geology.

On May 2, 1899, the directors of the Union Oil Company reached what later proved to be a crucial decision. It was to employ W. W. Orcutt, a young civil engineer inexperienced in the oil business, to look after the company's interests in Fresno and San Benito counties. They also decided to hire a "young man of good education and some geological knowledge and experience as a mountaineer to hunt for oil indications and seepages." This second young fellow employed by the company was Frank F. Hill, who soon emerged as drilling superintendent and later director of production. A condition was that both young men were to work for small salaries plus expenses. In Orcutt and Hill, Union acquired a team that made oil history.

Bill Orcutt founded the first geological department ever set up by any oil company. After a boyhood in Santa Paula, playing around the shops and wells of the Union Oil Company, Orcutt entered Stanford University with the first class, graduating in 1895 as a civil engineer and geologist, along with Herbert Hoover, who was awarded the same degree. Returning to Santa Paula, he worked for two and a half years as a civil and hydraulic engineer before landing his lifetime job with Union.

Hill, by way of contrast, was an experienced practical oil man. In his teens

*Cable tool drilling comes back into its own as Union Oil Company uses it in drilling shallow wells along Tar Creek and other Santa Paula areas. Here the driller and the tool dresser are "dumping the bailer" exactly as was done on same spot back in 1890.*

82

*Some wells have a long life. Tar Creek No. 1 drilled by Union Oil Company a half-century ago was still producing in 1950. A modern pumping unit has been placed at the well and a steel jackline stretched out to pump another well several hundred yards away.*

he had worked as a helper for Union Oil drilling crews, had rassled barrels and boxes and machinery around the warehouse, and delivered equipment. A Handy Andy with a genius for invention, Hill was forever coming up with an idea for doing something better. His greatest was one for cementing oil wells to keep out water. Cementing not only enabled drillers to go down deep to the big pools, but it doubled the amount of oil recovered from the sands. Cementing saved untold millions for the industry.

Hill hit on the idea while he was super-intendent of drilling crews in the Lompoc area. Water, flowing into the wells, slowed down production, threatening the very life of the field. Up to this time, drillers had used shavings, chopped rope, burlap, sacks, and other materials to try to close up the space between the casings and the walls of the holes. In some cases they even dumped in grain and beans, hoping that expansion of the seeds as they dampened might shut off the water. Frequently this worked temporarily, but eventually the water came back.

At Lompoc, the drillers tried everything

*This whirling Rotary Table spins some 200 revolutions a minute to keep a sharp bit cutting and grinding into the earth and rock thousands of feet below the surface as Union Oil Company seeks additional petroleum in its Santa Fe Springs field near Los Angeles.*

they could think of to cut off the water as the casings were driven deeper. Hill finally went over to the machine shop and asked the mechanics there to make a special bailer, one that would leave mud in holes instead of bailing it out. The mechanics told Hill he was crazy. But they built the bailer the way he wanted it anyway. Hill filled it with cement and lowered it to the bottom of the casing. There the cement was loosed. It shut off the running water temporarily but not permanently. The temporary success gave Hill a new idea. He next tried a packer at the bottom of the tubing. This enabled the crew to pump cement down into the well and up back of the casing. Out of this grew a whole series of ideas, sprouted by Hill and other Union drillers. Before long they had evolved a successful method of cementing behind the casing to shut out the water-bearing sands and leaving open only those strata that yielded oil. Ironically, Hill and other Union inventors were too busy to patent their ideas. Later on others took out patents, forcing the company to pay royalties on the ideas their crews originated.

*On the hills bordering expansive orange and lemon groves in the Santa Clara valley of California oil seekers, using the old cable tool method, begin pounding down a shallow well.*

86

*On sun-baked desert this driller watches drill stem. Mud hose hangs from rig at the left.*

Other oil producers realized, as soon as they learned of Hill's success in cementing oil wells, that in the future all wells must be cemented, because a field with cemented wells yielded twice as much oil as one in which the cementing was neglected. In the Santa Maria and Lompoc fields, they formed an association, later duplicated on other fields, known as the Producers Cementing Company, which tackled the problem of cementing out water for all wells. In time this voluntary agreement was superseded by a law, authorizing the state mineralogist to see that all oil wells were cemented.

Cementing wells soon became such a common practice that its importance in oil production is often overlooked. Without it, only half the oil produced in California in succeeding years would have been recovered. Hill's "crazy idea" was worth millions of dollars every day in crude delivered to the refineries.

There came a time, as drillers—Union's and those of Union's rivals—punched their holes deeper, when the old reliable cable and plunging bit would no longer do the job. The technique of banging holes deep into the earth hadn't changed much since the Chinese first hit on the spring-pole method for drilling their salt wells. The spring pole was simple and cheap and it got the California oil hunters off to a good start. In the early nineties, shortly after oil had been found under the surf in Santa Barbara County, the *Summerland Advance* commented that "the average cost of an oil well, all complete, is about $300. The running expense is $15 a month for each well. An ordinary well will yield 4 barrels per day or 120

87

barrels per month. One hundred twenty barrels are worth $125, leaving a balance each month of $110 from a $300 investment."

An oil well looked like the easy road to riches, and thousands of drillers set out to take it. All that was needed, so it appeared, was a site on which to drill, a long springy pole, a length of manila rope, a couple of hand-forged bits, a strong back, and a stronger pair of legs. The spring pole, suspended above the hole, yanked the bit upward. The drillers stepped on the treadle which sent it banging down again. Sinking a shallow well was fast and cheap, particularly in Pennsylvania or in the Los Angeles field, for example, where the oil was near the surface.

That was fine down to 600 or 700 feet. From that depth, the spring pole no longer yanked the bit up fast enough. So the drillers rigged up steam engines to turn bull wheels, which in turn rocked the walking beams that lifted heavier bits and banged them down, four times as fast as men hopping on and off treadles could do it. Thomas R. Bard, Union's first president, brought the first steam rig to California in the sixties. By 1890, when Union Oil was born, there were dozens of them snorting in the oil fields. When the drillers reached the 2,000-foot depth, the Manila ropes developed so much stretch that the walking beams no longer lifted and dropped the bits effectively. Steel cable solved that one, until

*To preserve such old rigs as this one with its wooden bull wheel, the California Oil Museum has been established at Santa Paula.*

*These great oil fields around Taft, California, burst into production five decades ago and wooden derricks still stand alongside the modern spidery steel rigs.*

the wells hit 5,000 feet. Then the steel in the cable became so heavy that the huffing steam engines had trouble lifting the weight. It looked as though the drillers had gone about as far as they could go.

Then the drillers took a new look at the newfangled rotary rigs that bored a hole in the earth the way bits bored into wood. The old-time California drillers had a poor opinion of rotaries. As early as 1889, the Western Prospecting Company of Denver tried a rotary rig to drill in Pico Canyon. After seventeen days of drilling, the bit was down only 60 feet. The drill was unable to cope with cobblestones buried in the earth. The crew finally finished a well, which yielded only 5½ barrels a day.

"It ought to give more," said the cable rig drillers, contending that the revolving bit sealed up the walls of the hole so that the oil couldn't trickle in. To prove it, they redrilled the hole with a steam cable rig. The well's output jumped to 20 barrels a day.

That experience and the legends which grew out of it kept rotary rigs out of the California fields for nearly two decades. In the new Texas fields, where rocks were few and the oil was deep, the rotary drilling rigs were popular. By 1906, when they again appeared in California to tap the deep San Joaquin Valley sands that the steam cable drillers couldn't reach,

rotaries were bigger and stronger, had sharper teeth. The Texans knew how to handle them. But in the Santa Fe Springs field, where Union first tried a rotary drill in 1907, the Texans were baffled by California's eccentric geology. At 350 feet they gave up. Then Frank Hill came up with one of his inevitable ideas, a combination steam cable and rotary rig. His drillers went for the compromise. They banged down hole as far as they could go with cable, then bored the hole from there on. They passed the 1-mile depth, a milestone in the Black Bonanza, and tapped oil pools that yielded up to 3,000 barrels a day per well.

In succeeding years the tool men made bigger bits of tougher metals, stepped up the rotary speed from 50 to 400 revolutions per minute, utilized the weight of the shaft to grind through any formation, however hard. They passed the 2-mile, the 3-mile depth, finally pushed their holes to the fantastic depth of 21,000 feet, almost 4 miles into the earth. As they pushed deeper, probing for the deep pools, the time came when a single hole cost a million dollars, more than half the total resources of the four oil companies that merged in 1890 to become the Union Oil Company of California.

California was still Wildcatters' Paradise, but they had to be mighty wellheeled wildcatters.

# CHAPTER SIX

# Men against Men

WHILE Union's grimy drilling crews probed for the ocean of oil under California's sedimentary soils, Union's management was hitting oceans of trouble, in the home office, in the refinery, in the markets, and in the money marts. The company's executives didn't have to prospect for this ocean of trouble; it swept over them in tides—tides of human frailties, rivalries, and animosities. And there were tides of debts that nearly swamped the fledgling company.

Trouble began almost the day the Union Oil Company of California was born, October 17, 1890. In the very incorporation was planted the yeast of dissent which fermented into a fight to the finish between two strong-willed founders with diametrically opposite philosophies as to the destiny of the company. President Thomas R. Bard wanted to mine the oil out of the company's properties, sell it wholesale, and cash in. Lyman Stewart considered it his destiny to found an oil empire that would endure for generations.

The shotgun merger by which four little oil companies were wedded into one sizeable corporation merely maintained the teeter-totter balance of power between the Bard interests and the Stewart-Hardison group. What prompted the merger was an option agreement with Daniel Dull of New York and Ambrose C. Burdick of Chicago. Union's founders agreed to sell 49 per cent of the combined Bard-Stewart-Hardison oil properties to the Dull-Burdick syndicate; Dull and Burdick offered in return $800,000 and a half interest in a revolutionary new refining process developed by Dr. Frederick Salathe, a distinguished Swiss chemist. By this process at an additional cost of 5 cents per barrel of crude, Union's refinery would be able to turn out water-white kerosene as good as that with which Standard Oil Company captured the lion's share of the illuminant market on the Pacific Coast. Dull and Burdick guaranteed that the process would assure Union a net return of $3.25 per barrel from petroleum products.

It was too good to believe. It was too

*Heavy drilling equipment used in nineties was made and kept in repair at the Santa Paula shops of Union Oil. Here are some of the crew: standing, Billy McGee, Frank Preston, Lou Spitler (with cap), Phil Nickles (with hat), Fred Richardson, Ed Larson, Jack Reddick, Charlie Wacksmith, Johnny Bottom, and two unidentified; sitting, Frank Dinger, Joe Krepser, Billy Robertson and Billy Jones.*

good—period. Dull and Burdick never exercised their option. They had promised more than they could deliver. It was only the first of many rainbows of high finance for which the Union founders grasped before the management settled down to build an oil empire the hard but sure way.

The Dull-Burdick rainbow had one lasting result. Before the option expired, Bard, Stewart, and Hardison carried out their part of the bargain by consolidating the Hardison & Stewart Oil Company and its subsidiary, the Mission Transfer Company, with the Sespe Oil Company and the Torrey Canyon Oil Company. It was obviously a phony merger. The four little oil corporations were kept intact on the books, merely exchanging their stock for Union Oil Company stock and turning their properties over to Union for development and operation.

In this half merger sprouted the seeds of dissent. Thomas R. Bard was president of the new Union Oil Company of California; of Mission Transfer, the marketing concern; and of the Sespe and Torrey Canyon companies, strictly oil-producing concerns. Lyman Stewart was president of the Hardison & Stewart Oil Company, which owned Mission Transfer outright. He and Hardison controlled Sespe Oil Company through stock ownership.

In the issue of Union Oil Company stock, on the basis of an appraisal of real property value of the four merged companies, Hardison & Stewart Oil Com-

92

pany got 29,912 shares, with a book value of $2,191,579. This was 53 per cent, and control of Union Oil on the basis of stockholdings. Sespe Oil Company received 20,581 shares, Torrey Canyon Oil got 7,498 shares, the two together holding 47 per cent of Union Oil.

But, and it was a big, doubtful "but," as events proved, Bard by agreement was allowed to name a majority of the directors of both Sespe and Torrey Canyon boards, which in turn enabled him to hold a slight edge on the Union Oil board. The five-man "Bard Camp" consisted of President Bard, Secretary I. H. Warring, Directors Dan McFarland, W. S. Chaffee, and Casper Taylor. The four-man "Stewart Group" included Vice-president Lyman Stewart, Treasurer Wallace L. Hardison, Directors John Irwin and Alexander Waldie.

Thus the stage was set for an eight-year battle. As president, Bard had the authority to run the new company, which he did with a high hand—when he was on the job. But Bard's other extensive interests and political activities on a national scale, culminating in his appointment as United States senator, called him away frequently, sometimes for extended periods. When Bard was absent, Vice-president Stewart stepped into the managerial shoes. He, too, ran Union Oil with a high hand. Often the alternate bosses

*Proud workmen in Santa Paula shops of Union Oil built this steam engine in 1896. From this start developed the great Union Tool Company. Among the workmen were, left to right, George Witmer, Ed Nelson, two unidentified, Billy Robertson, Fred Jones, Bill Woods, Joe Merrick. Bottom row: B. N. Youngken, Fred Stewart and Billy Frey.*

of Union Oil reversed each other's and the company's policies.

Asked why he and Hardison had voted for Bard for president in the first place, Lyman Stewart once replied, "Mr. Bard was a man of great wealth and influence. We regarded him as a multimillionaire, while all the rest of us combined could not have approached a million at the time."

In 1890, Lyman Stewart had few silver dollars to jingle. Hardison was almost as hard up for cash. In eight years as oil producers and sellers, neither had drawn a dollar in dividends for his work. Neither drew a salary. Stewart's personal income came from occasional dividends from Pennsylvania oil leases in which the family was interested. Ironically, rich Mr. Bard was voted a $5,000-a-year salary as president. The impoverished vice-president, Mr. Stewart, drew no salary—even when he took over as manager during Bard's frequent absences from duty.

Almost immediately, Bard and Stewart clashed on policy. Stewart wanted to expand not only in the field by buying and leasing new oil lands while they were cheap but by building new markets, pipelines, tankers, expanding refinery capacity, improving products. Bard's idea was that Union should remain a producing oil company, drilling wells, pumping petroleum, selling to outlets at wholesale and letting them have the headaches of refining and marketing. The clashes over policy soon grew into personal animosity as each side strove to control the destiny of Union Oil Company.

As vice-president, Lyman Stewart drove the drillers in the field, prodded the company's representatives and dealers in cities, fought for better rail rates, crusaded for oil as a fuel in California industry, wangled loans, exhorted the refinery workers at Santa Paula to turn out better kerosene, fuel oil, and lubricants.

Although he was hard pressed all the time and drawing no salary from Union for his work on the company's behalf, Lyman Stewart favored investing more and more Union money in oil lands, pipelines, refineries, and marketing facilities. Stewart's policy for years was to invest $2 in resources for each dollar distributed as dividends. His old partner Wallace Hardison, who had branched out into farming, horse raising, and politics, didn't share this view, complaining in July, 1890, "I think it is about time that we looked after our own households. It has now been eight years since we commenced to make our investments, and putting our time in this business, and we have not received in dividends one cent."

Bard shared this view, too.

Bard's man Friday was I. H. Warring, who became bookkeeper and secretary of the company. Born in Piru, near Santa Paula, Warring had started as a bookkeeper for the Mission Transfer Company when Bard organized it. Being at headquarters, he assumed the duties of general manager when Bard was away, clashing frequently with Lyman Stewart, who was next in line in authority, and often arbitrarily canceling deals that Stewart made in the markets. A petulant busybody, Warring snooped on Stewart and Hardison and reported to Bard everything that they did. As time passed, Warring developed a special animosity for Lyman Stewart.

94

*Santa Paula refinery erected in 1887 by the Hardison & Stewart Oil Co. Plant had a capacity throughput its first year of about 14,000 barrels, turning out such products as asphaltum, lubricants, greases and illuminating oils. Refinery was destroyed by fire but rebuilt.*

In the fight for California markets competition was getting keener. This was particularly true in San Francisco, largest outlet for oil on the coast. There Eastern competition was offering kerosene hauled across the country at prices lower than the cost of making and transporting illuminating oils in California. In July, 1890, T. J. Cochrane, manager of the Mission Transfer Company San Francisco office, reported that "the Standard are preparing for war west of the Rockies, and soon there will be firing all along the line. They now have a pipeline from the Ohio fields and the Pennsylvania fields to Chicago. There they are building the largest oil refinery in the world, with a view to furnishing the Far West. They will refine a mixture of the oils, a viscose, and it will be a cheap oil and fairly good. Being 600 miles nearer to the market than any other oil manufactured by their competitors,

they will get a lower freight rate. They will, of course, get the usual rebate. Taking it all in all, they will cut the life out of our prices within a year. Some of the Standard men are here now."

That meant more trouble for the new Union Oil Company. To gird Union for war, Lyman Stewart introduced a resolution at the next board meeting that "immediate steps be taken to secure the services of a competent analytical and manufacturing chemist." Stewart found the man whom he thought Union needed. He was S. J. Carman of Bradford, Pennsylvania, an experienced and practical oil chemist.

President Bard ignored Stewart's suggestion that Union hire Carman. Instead, Bard hired Dr. Frederick Salathe, the chemist who had been hailed as the discoverer of the process by which Dull and Burdick claimed to get a much higher

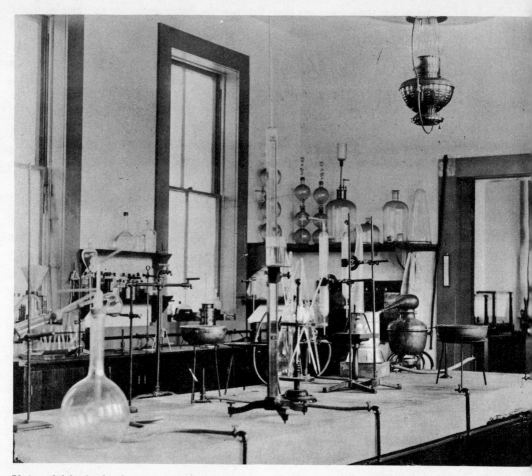

*Union Oil built the first petroleum laboratory in the West in 1891. This is believed to be a picture of the room in which Dr. Salathe began his study of Western oils.*

percentage of kerosene from crude oil, at the then fabulous salary of $10,000 a year, plus a bonus. Trained in Switzerland, the temperamental doctor held a very high opinion of himself and his skill as a chemist. Though he had been warned not to give Salathe the reins of an executive position, Bard made him boss, not only of the new $3,500 laboratory, the first fullfledged petroleum laboratory west

of the Mississippi, but also of the refinery at Santa Paula.

Dr. Salathe turned out to be an experimenter and not a production man. Before long the refinery operation was in a complete state of confusion. One of the first things the doctor did was to cancel the system of daily reports from the manufacturing branch to the marketing people. As a result Lyman Stewart and Union's deal-

96

ers no longer knew what the company had to sell. One of Dr. Salathe's enthusiasms was an improved sewing-machine oil. He made up 300 barrels of the stuff, enough to supply the Pacific Coast for a decade. After several years, the surplus had to be dumped.

Bard decided on a shake-up in the marketing branch of the company's operation. The first to get the ax was T. J. Cochrane, the San Francisco agent who had built up an excellent trade in the Bay area. He was fired early in 1891. Sales promptly fell off so much that the company had to shut down the refinery at Santa Paula for a period. Over Stewart's protests the board of directors sustained Bard. The latter followed by canceling the company's contract with the Los Angeles Oil Burning and Supply Company, which had handled Union's products exclusively in the Los Angeles market. Thus, Union faced a sharp drop in business in both of its major markets simultaneously.

Paradoxically, the company for once had money in the bank. Stewart wanted to use this cash to buy more oil lands, to expand the refinery, and to build a pipeline from Ventura to Los Angeles. However, his old partner Hardison, supported by Bard, persuaded the directors to vote regular monthly cash dividends of $10,000, plus a stock dividend of $30,-000. The dividends were started in May, 1891, and they were the first returns that either Stewart or Hardison had received in the eight years since they launched their oil hunt in California in 1883.

Suddenly, late in 1891, Union found itself menaced on a new front. Assembly Bill 210, introduced in the state legislature in Sacramento, established new and rigid specifications for kerosene which Western refiners could not meet. The bill, sponsored by Eastern oil interests, was a sleeper. With its passage, the illuminating-oil market would become a Standard monopoly, because Western refiners could not meet the specifications established for kerosene. Luckily, Thomas Bard was a powerful political figure as well as a shrewd and aggressive businessman. Hardison, too, had dabbled in politics and knew his way around. They went to work on the legislature. "If this bill becomes a law," Bard wrote, "all opposition to the Standard Oil Company in this state of California will cease and the monopoly will be complete in the state, and more perfect than in any other state." Union managed to build up sufficient pressure to prevent the bill from becoming a law, and one more hurdle had been passed.

Hardly had this threat been erased when another one arose in its place. This was a prospective lawsuit by another firm in San Francisco, calling itself the Union Oil Company. It had been doing business for several years as a partnership. The San Francisco Union Oil Company had never been incorporated. Bard pointed out to the copartners that the new company's name was the Union Oil Company of California and that it had been incorporated, whereas the other had not. He persuaded them to call off their suit and quit calling themselves the Union Oil Company. At the time, there was still another Union Oil Company in Pennsylvania, a flourishing and highly profitable concern founded in the 1870s. This, too, later disappeared from the scene.

When the option to Dull and Burdick expired, President Bard entered into negotiations with J. B. Livingstone, president of the Standard Paint Company of New York, who proposed to organize a new company to take over Union's refinery and handle not only the refining but the marketing of the products made from Union's crude. Bard and Stewart immediately clashed over this project. Under the deal with Livingstone, Union would own one-half of the new company and the Standard Paint Company would own the rest. The deal fell through and the showdown clash between Bard and Lyman Stewart was postponed until another year.

Union plunged into a new venture, making printers' ink at the Santa Paula refinery. This was Hardison's pet enthusiasm. On November 18, 1891, the California Ink Company was organized by Lyman Stewart, W. L. Hardison, Thomas R. Bard, Alexander Waldie, and I. H. Warring, with a capitalization of $200,-000, consisting of 2,000 shares of $100 par. It was sleight-of-hand incorporation, because on the afternoon of the ink company's founding the Union Oil Company bought the decoy little California Ink Company, along with all its patents and other rights. Union's directors operated California Ink as a separate entity, agreeing to advance money, not to exceed $10,000 at 9 per cent, from time to time to enable the new concern to get under

way. To finance this deal, Union had to get more loans from the Bank of Hueneme, the First National Bank of Los Angeles, and the First National Bank of Santa Paula.

Stewart kept picking up acreage here, a lease there. Buying land or leasing it was his particular enthusiasm. This President Bard disapproved. Bard also became increasingly irritated over the losses incurred by the experimental work being done in the refinery. Stewart and Hardison, for their part, were beginning to sense that there was a lot more in a barrel of oil than some fuel oil, some kerosene, some asphalt, and some grease. Late in 1891 they turned down a proposition from the Standard Oil Company to handle all of Union's naphtha and gasoline production, although there was so little of the latter that when A. D. Williams of Santa Barbara tried to get a drum of it from the Mission Transfer Company in July, 1890, he was informed that "just at this time we have none in stock and it will probably be several days before we make any more. As soon as we have some we will advise you." About a month later the refinery was able to report that "we expect to make at least a drum of gasoline by Thursday of next week."

Writing to the Standard management, Lyman Stewart bluffed, "We are expected by our customers to fill orders for all kinds of our refinery products, and we

---

*Los Angeles City Field about 1895 had "wells as thick as holes in a pepper pot" and the estimate of 3,000 wells in a narrow strip of land only 4½ miles long seems not far wrong. This boom was touched off in 1893 by Edward L. Doheny who dug a successful wildcat near downtown Los Angeles. Years later he served as a director of Union Oil and twice sought to buy it.*

cannot believe that it would be to our advantage to ask you to handle for us our entire output of any one or a few of our products, especially such as meet with so ready a sale at a satisfactory price as do our naphthas and gasoline."

Unable to induce the directors to vote the Union Oil Company out of the marketing business, Bard made the refinery the special target of his barbed antipathy. F. H. Dunham, the superintendent, found himself on the receiving end of a series of annoying memos.

"It will be your duty to keep the gates of the refinery under lock at all times," Bard wrote Dunham. "You will report once a week the names of the persons admitted to the yard. You are enjoined from emparting to any one any information relating to the work of your own or any other department of the company's business, except as you may be permitted to do so under special written instructions."

In June, 1892, Bard informed the directors he had decided to discharge Dunham, and with diabolical finesse he delegated Vice-president Stewart, who had backed Dunham to the limit, in various clashes with Bard and with Dr. Salathe, as the committee to notify Dunham that he was ousted.

By the end of 1891, under Lyman Stewart's driving, Union's wells had produced that year 111,901 barrels of oil, more than one-third of the state's output of 323,600 barrels that year. To gain this remarkable production, Stewart had moved the drilling rigs from the Ex-Mission lands formerly controlled by Hardison and Stewart and had put down eight fine producing wells on the property of the Torrey Canyon Oil Company, controlled by Bard. These wells alone brought

*Birthplace of Union Oil was on the second floor corner office of this building in Santa Paula, California. Offices of the Ventura Division of the company are here. The California Oil Museum, with its priceless collection, now occupies the entire first floor.*

in 70,000 barrels that year. This production made Union dependent on Torrey Canyon oil and gave Bard a new weapon, which he later used on Stewart. It was cheap oil. The drilling costs had been held down. Labor costs were about one-third of the expense of each well, running from $475 to $1,315. With this inexpensive oil Stewart hoped to meet the new competition for the San Francisco market.

Stewart was still picking up new leases, some in the San Joaquin Valley. To get into the new Los Angeles field, Stewart persuaded the directors to buy the Los Angeles Oil Company. This was Union's first production outside of Ventura County. One excellent well produced 15,000 barrels in the first twelve months. But the bottom dropped out of Los Angeles oil, and Stewart found it cheaper to buy oil than to pump it. He had guessed wrong and was repeatedly reminded of it by Warring.

To finance this expansion, Union directors were forced to authorize Stewart to borrow many thousands of dollars. They did it over the opposition of President Bard. Stewart spent most of his time out in the field, prodding the drillers and hunting promising new oil lands. The company desperately needed production of crude to offset the constant demands of bankers for repayment of various notes. Then, in February 1892, Lyman Stewart's dream was realized as Adams No. 28 came in with a roar.

This was Stewart's answer to the skeptics—oil in quantities. A wave of optimism swept the company. On May of that year the directors granted an option to Colonel J. M. Marble, the Los Angeles broker, to sell within three months 15,000 shares of preferred and 30,000 shares of common stock of a new Union Oil Company of New Jersey, a state which permitted issuance of preferred shares. This new subsidiary was to enable Union to expand in pace with the new discoveries of oil in the California fields. Although this high-finance scheme fell through, it was the forerunner of more stock-juggling devices that were to confuse the Union Oil financial picture for the next two decades. Union was perpetually broke; its directors were forever grasping at financial straws.

Meantime, Dr. Salathe was running the refinery at Santa Paula with a high hand. Despite the promises of more and better kerosene at lower cost, the doctor was more interested in experiment than actual refining for the trade and was making little headway in producing salable merchandise. Stewart wanted products to sell.

"I think the policy of the company in running the refinery should be to make such products as the trade requires," Stewart told Secretary Warring. "Also to put such a price on them as to make them compete with other goods from similar sources."

In an effort to recoup in the Los Angeles market, where the Los Angeles Oil Burning and Supply Company contract had been terminated, Stewart opened a small sales office on East Second Street. It was little more than a hole in the wall, and though the directors approved the sales office, Bard at least tacitly, it soon became a major bone of contention between Vice-president Stewart and Secretary Warring, who was convinced the small rental was a waste of the company's money. Warring made such an issue over the Los Angeles office that Stewart finally took it to the board. The directors sustained him, but even this clean-cut decision failed to smooth out the differences between the two camps.

Warring overlooked no opening to clip Stewart. This feuding frequently cost Union business the company badly needed. Among the people Stewart had persuaded to try oil for fuel was fiery General M. H. Sherman, president of the Los Angeles Consolidated Railway Electric Company. Sherman agreed to switch from coal to oil in his shops. The experiment was working out well when President Bard, prodded by Warring, sent a sharp letter to the general, who was having his own troubles keeping the streetcars rolling.

"We thought that we had fully explained to you that it was impossible for us to deviate from our uniform rule of collecting in full monthly," wrote Bard. "While we hope to continue to enjoy your custom, we certainly shall decline your orders unless we can be insured against any inconvenience occasioned by dilatory payments."

The general promptly switched his "custom" to one of Union's competitors and later went back to coal.

Came the panic of 1893, accompanied

101

*Old-time jacklines pumping ancient wells, like the one shown here, may still be seen in some California oil fields.*

by the burst of oil production in the Los Angeles fields following the Doheny discoveries. Oil operators failed right and left. Union was forced into severe retrenchment to survive. On one black day the company had to borrow from three different banks, from an individual, and from the estate of a recently deceased friend of the company. To make matters worse, Dr. Salathe chose this particular moment to go on a buying spree for new laboratory equipment, tying up thousands of dollars that Union didn't have.

Warring renewed his sniping at Lyman Stewart, becoming so belligerent that he wrote to President Bard:

"I am inclined to think that we made a serious mistake when we employed Mr. Stewart to look after our fuel business for the reason that he is too anxious to sell his burners."

Stewart's reply to the panic was a drive for new business. He demonstrated and sold the new aerated oil-fuel burner to anyone who would listen, pointing to the saving in fuel in Los Angeles industries already trying out the revolutionary innovation. The Southern Pacific had turned a deaf ear to his pleas for lower freight rates, and a pipeline from Ventura to Los Angeles looked like the only way to compete on even terms in the Los Angeles market. Bard and Warring persuaded the directors to veto the idea. They also decided to suspend dividends, causing much clamoring from stockholders.

South American oil was pouring into the California markets by tanker. Wallace Hardison, after selling nearly all of his Union Oil stock, had gone to South America to hunt oil, teaming up with W. R. Grace & Company, which had outfitted a large tanker to transport oil from Peru to San Francisco up the Pacific Coast. This tanker could handle 35,000 barrels of oil on each trip. Every time it hove in the Golden Gate, oil prices slumped.

Union had another acute problem in its major market, San Francisco. The company had to refine its crude at Santa Paula, where Warring had arbitrarily taken over direction of the little rundown refinery. The quality of Union's fuel oil deterio-

*First refinery crew at Santa Paula in 1887 managed to turn out fair quantities of asphalt and fuel oil but rarely a barrel of gasoline. After the refinery burned, some parts of it were shipped to the Oleum refinery on San Francisco Bay.*

rated so seriously that steamship owners whom Stewart had persuaded to convert from coal to oil complained of the fires under their boilers going out because of the amount of water in the fuel. The Cudahy Packing Company in Los Angeles had so much trouble with Union's fuel oil that they went over to a competitor. When Stewart complained that poor products were losing Union's best customers, Warring replied, "If you wish to take the position, as intimated in your letter, that the writer is sole manager of the refinery and as such manager is responsible for every barrel shipped, then it will be necessary to change the management of the refinery."

This was the moment for which Stewart had waited. Dr. Salathe's contract had expired and not even Bard wanted to renew it. Taking Warring at his word, Stewart persuaded the board to "change the management" at the refinery. Professor S. F. Peckham, an experienced University of California chemist, was placed in charge. The professor launched a cleanup, and the quality of Union's products improved immediately. Even so, the company was desperately in need of a new refinery. Stewart wanted it built in one of the big markets, either in the Los Angeles area or in the San Francisco Bay region. He also wanted Union to buy out the Los Angeles Oil Burning and Supply Company, which was rapidly capturing much of Union's business in the Southern California market. But before a deal could be worked out, the negotiations broke down. Meanwhile Stewart scouted in both the Los Angeles and San Francisco areas for a new refinery site. This imminent expansion program, which had the approval of the majority of the directors, was so distasteful to President Bard that he, without warning, presented his resignation as president of the company in protest. On Stewart's motion the board declined to accept the resignation, and Bard stayed on.

At this same meeting, Stewart quit as sales manager in Los Angeles. It was ten years since he had left the Pennsylvania oil fields, and he wanted to make a trip East on family affairs. Before departing, he launched young Will Stewart, who had completed two years at the University of California, where he had made a great record as an athlete, in the oil game. Will had worked during the summer vacations as a roustabout for drilling crews. To learn refining and marketing as well as production, Lyman Stewart arranged for Will to work in the refinery at $75 a month. When Will reported for work, Warring took charge of his education. When Lyman Stewart returned from the East after several months, he found young Will had

done nothing but cooper barrels. Angry, Lyman Stewart protested Warring's highhand instructions to Dr. Peckham that young Will was to be kept outside the refinery.

The rival cofounders of Union Oil soon had it out in a heated argument, in the course of which Bard stated that he intended to do everything in his power to defeat the ambitions of the Stewart family. Bard had almost succeeded in eliminating the Stewarts at a board meeting on July 24, 1894, when both W. L. Hardison and Lyman Stewart were absent. This was the opportunity for which Bard and Warring had been waiting. Bard persuaded the board to accept his resignation and elect his man, D. T. Perkins, as president, with Warring as general manager of the entire company. Neither Stewart nor Hardison had any warning of this maneuver.

It was a furious Lyman Stewart who returned from the East a short time later to find Union Oil reorganized along Bard lines. Stewart lost no time lining up his voting strength. Three months later, at the annual meeting in October, 1894, Stewart was ready for a showdown. When the new officers were chosen, he was named not only president but general manager as well. This made him boss of the company which Bard had run for four years. Now it was Lyman Stewart's turn. As Bard came out of the meeting, he said to Stewart, "Well, you have us where you want us now."

Stewart replied in a conciliatory vein, offering to let Bard name five of the nine directors if the ex-president would agree not to hamper the new management. Bard accepted, thereby setting the stage for renewed rivalry and a still more important showdown.

In the driver's seat at last, Lyman Stewart exploited his ideas for marketing oil products. He lost no time in launching the new company policy; calling a special meeting of the board, he asked the directors to listen to some unpleasant truth from Professor Peckham, who was working on the new illuminant with which Stewart hoped to compete on equal terms with Eastern oils.

"The trouble with California oil is that no one knows anything about it," Peckham told the directors. "We do not know what we have been working on, and the results of our labor thus far have been sort of thrusts in the dark." Peckham proposed to remove some of the darkness and the guessing. Impressed, the directors asked the professor to stay with the company for as long as he could do so, at a salary of $333 per month.

During the first month of his administration, Stewart launched plans for a new barge with a capacity of 5,000 barrels. He opened an aggressive campaign to have oil displace coal as fuel for all Pacific Coast industry. He tackled the railroads vigorously, demanding lower rates and threatening to build pipelines to transport Union's oil to the Los Angeles and San Francisco areas. Accepting the challenge of the Grace-Hardison combination, which had hired not only Dr. Salathe but also A. C. Hardison, Union's former pipeline superintendent, and built a small refinery for Peruvian oil in the San Francisco Bay area, Stewart rehired F. H. Dunham, the

*D. T. Perkins, the second president of Union Oil, served only from July to October, 1894.*

efficient former superintendent of the refinery who had been fired by Bard, to make the Santa Paula refinery produce more efficiently.

The year 1894 proved a turning point for Union. Stewart's campaign to make oil the fuel for California industry was bearing fruit. The Los Angeles Iron and Steel Company reported that by using oil it had cut its fuel costs 50 per cent in comparison with coal. The *Los Angeles Times* reported that oil was being used for baking brick, for smelting, and in fact for any of the mechanical arts in which a high heat was necessary. The *Times* even

105

tossed a neat editorial bouquet, reporting that "Union Oil Company has long been known as the 'Old Reliable.' Union makes it a special business to introduce oil for any new work wherein oil has not been used before, and puts forth every effort to make a success of the same."

By 1895 Lyman Stewart could be proud of his first year as head of Union. He had done an effective job of marketing in Los Angeles and elsewhere in California. But he had not been able to find enough money to build his cherished and long-planned pipeline from Ventura to Los Angeles, nor had he been able to build the new refinery he wanted to turn out

better products and more of them. The flood of cheap oil from the Los Angeles fields had forced the Santa Paula wells to almost shut down. Stewart wanted his new refinery near the market. Bard, as a director and large stockholder, was still a power behind the scenes, working through Warring and the other directors. But even Bard was beginning to see for the first time the importance of marketing. The board named Bard and Stewart as a committee to check possible tidewater sites for a new refinery. The two studied San Francisco, Ventura, Hueneme, and Los Angeles harbor facilities. After the survey, Stewart reported, "If we would locate in

Ventura, we would have no influence on the business in Los Angeles, and someone else would also be sure to occupy this field. The result would be that we would not be in it here or in San Francisco. We know now that the San Francisco field is occupied and this one is not. One way to hold this ground is to occupy it."

With a prophetic viewpoint not shared by many at the time, he continued, "Los Angeles is to be the great city of the future, and if we occupy the ground now we may be able to lead in this business and control a market for such products as we can make right along for years to come. But we need to study the whole ground over and be united and decide in reference to the location."

Although Bard and the other directors sustained him, Union didn't locate in Los Angeles, where the city fathers protested that a refinery and the necessary storage tanks would be a great fire hazard to the city. Their opposition grew so vociferous that Lyman Stewart turned north. For $15,000 he bought a sizeable parcel of Rancho El Chino, the site that he and Bard had picked out when they visited San Francisco Bay, from the California Redwood Company. He ordered new equipment from Pennsylvania and made plans to move the company's refining operations from Santa Paula. Then, greatly to his astonishment, Bard, who had joined him in choosing the site, vehemently objected to moving the refinery.

The board meeting sustained Stewart, but as a sop to Bard agreed to his demand that Union sell the California Ink Company. The business, which later grew into a substantial industry, was dumped for $16,000, far less than the Union Oil Company had invested in it.

Adopting new tactics to frustrate Lyman Stewart's spending, Bard notified the directors that he would propose at the next board meeting that the company extinguish its debts by assessment on its stockholders. This was a shrewd move. Bard had millions behind him. The Stewarts were still oil-poor, embarrassed by a lack of cash. Fortunately, before Bard had an opportunity to present this proposal to the board, Union sold a lot of oil and was out of debt for once. Stewart was able to go to his old friend I. W. Hellman, by this time president of the Nevada Bank in San Francisco, and arrange for new loans for expansion. This time Stewart had more than hopes to offer the banker for security.

"As collateral, we propose to give $40,000 worth of stock of the Mission Transfer Company, which is capitalized at $250,000 but which actually has paid in cash capital of $480,000 and has a yearly income of $48,000," he told Hellman. "The Mission Transfer Company is entirely free from debt, and we believe its stock to be a No. 1 security. The Union Oil Company is also out of debt, but is making additions to its plant which will require more capital than will be available

*Pride of the Oleum Refinery when it opened on San Francisco Bay in 1896 were these four stills with a daily capacity of 150 barrels each. Today Oleum has a throughput capacity of around 60,000 barrels a day, turning out scores of petroleum products.*

107

from its current income. It has some 80,000 barrels of oil on hand in its tanks, a daily production of some 600 barrels, and has many thousands of acres of oil lands which are worth several million dollars from an oil man's standpoint. During the past four years Union has paid in cash dividends to its stockholders $320,000."

The double duties of being president and general manager of Union Oil were proving too arduous for Lyman Stewart, whose health was not good. Bard was clamoring against the Stewart management and demanding appointment of a general manager apart from the presidency. On August 22, 1895, Stewart resigned as general manager, and F. L. Richardson was chosen for the office at a salary of $3,000 a year. Richardson was not experienced in the oil business and admitted it. He quickly organized committees and appointed chairmen, with Lyman Stewart heading the field department; Bard, the pipeline, storage, and transportation departments; W. L. Stewart, the son of the president, who had been appointed a director, heading the Los Angeles office; D. T. Perkins in charge of the refinery operations.

Richardson had hardly taken over his new duties of general manager when he died suddenly. All the burdensome chores fell again on the shoulders of Lyman Stewart, who was reelected both president and general manager. His salary for the double job was $250 a month.

Late that year at the annual meeting the smoldering feud between Stewart and Bard broke out anew. Fed up with the sniping of I. H. Warring, Stewart demanded that he be ousted as secretary.

Unable to attend the meeting, Bard evidently had some inkling of Stewart's intentions. He filed a protest even before Stewart offered his reorganization program for the coming year. The directors backed Stewart. Warring was out, and Bard no longer had his man Friday in the key position.

For some time Bard and Stewart had seldom agreed on anything. There was no longer an effort on either side to cover up mutually antagonistic feelings. Stewart proceeded to appoint a Stewart staff to run Union Oil. When the Oleum refinery on San Francisco Bay was finished in February, 1896, Stewart placed it under the direction of Frederick L. King, whom he had employed as the new San Francisco manager. Bard had no use for King and moved that the board repudiate Stewart's choice. The board sustained Stewart, who soon wished that it had overruled him. King proved to be the weak link in Stewart's chain of command. Though the new refinery was the last word in plants for making petroleum products, it failed to show a profit. Stewart transferred F. H. Dunham, his veteran refinery man at Santa Paula, to Oleum to straighten things out. Bard was still bitter about the transfer of refinery operation from Santa Paula to Oleum. On the night of June 29, 1896, fire gutted the old Santa Paula plant. Oleum was the only place Union could refine.

At this time much of Union's oil came from wells and tunnels near Santa Paula and from several wells in the Los Angeles area. Stewart chartered the barge "Enoch Talbot" to carry oil from Ventura to Oleum. Business in the San Francisco

108

market was growing by leaps and bounds. It was so good, in fact, that in 1896 H. C. Breeden, a San Francisco financier representing the Standard Oil Company, made an offer to purchase 51 per cent of the stock of the Union Oil Company. Stewart refused to consider the offer unless Standard agreed to buy the entire company. Standard balked at this idea.

Standard retaliated by cutting prices of kerosene. Lyman Stewart wrote to his brother Milton late in that year to see if Union could import oil from Pennsylvania to mix with Union's kerosene to upgrade the Western product. He also fought back by stepping up drilling and increasing deliveries, contracting with the Pacific Coast Oil Company for the surplus capacity of its new tanker, the "George Loomis," to move fuel oil from the Ventura field to San Francisco. Unfortunately Union was unable always to supply enough oil to fill its share of the "Loomis's" tanks. Bad feeling developed when Pacific Coast Oil Company tried to squeeze Stewart out of the Watsonville market, where beet-sugar mills were big fuel users. Foreseeing this squeeze coming, Stewart had ordered an 8,000-barrel barge. It was lucky he did, because shortly Standard Oil bought the Pacific Coast Oil Company, and the "Loomis" was no longer available to Union.

By the middle of 1897 Lyman Stewart was forced to admit that Bard was right about Frederick King, the San Francisco manager. King had discharged not only F. H. Dunham, the Oleum manager, but nearly everyone else who knew anything about California oil. When Stewart visited the refinery, the only employee he recognized was the night watchman. Stewart replaced King with John Baker, Jr., who became a driving force and one of the great oil salesmen on the Pacific Coast.

That year the hectic California oil boom took a new turn. The Los Angeles fields, which had been pouring out an ocean of oil at low prices, were suddenly played out. Production fell off so drastically that railroad locomotives had to be reconverted back to coal. Oil was still a feast or famine business. By the end of the year, it was swinging back to feast again, with the discovery of a new field at Whittier, east of Los Angeles. Union was still so short of oil that Stewart offered a bonus to drilling crews.

The directors, in 1897, employed R. W. Fenn, a civil engineer and a director in Bard's Torrey Canyon Oil Company, to make a survey of Union properties. Fenn's report was something of a sensation. It showed how tankers would have saved Union much of the $600,000 paid in freight to San Francisco during the past six years. Pipelines would have saved the company's Los Angeles market. A company-owned tool and supply house would have saved Union a sizeable fortune.

Impressed by Fenn's report, the directors authorized Stewart to build a 10,000-barrel tanker. But Bard managed to stymie appropriations for the pipeline or the tool company. The latter had an interesting background, dating from the flood of oil from the Los Angeles City field that ruined Union's market temporarily. Realizing that he had missed out in this field, Stewart tried to recoup by expanding Union's tool shop in Santa Paula with a branch which would sell tools, pipe, and

109

*Jackline plant in Wild Bill Canyon pumps a dozen wells by means of steel cables running out from a revolving eccentric which alternately pulls and releases the cables which, in turn, operate the pumps. One central power plant can serve many wells over long distances.*

machinery to the hundreds of Los Angeles wildcatters. Union's tool dressers and machinists had built up a great reputation as mechanical wizards who could redesign or modify almost any kind of oil-field machinery. The Hardison & Stewart Oil Company had also founded the Santa Paula Hardware Company, which served as a supply department as well as a hardware store. Bard not only headed off Stewart's dream of an oil-tool branch, but persuaded the directors to sell the hard-

ware store to W. T. McFie, the manager, who opened up in Los Angeles under the name McFie & Herron, building an important oil-well supply house.

Stewart bided time. In 1895, he began sounding out manufacturers on the possibility of buying supplies not only for Union but other oil companies. The American Tube Works agreed to sell at factory prices, if Union would establish a separate company to handle the deal. The National Tube Company agreed to supply the ma-

110

terials Union's crews needed that year at a saving of around $23,000 if a subsidiary were set up to handle the business. Stewart tossed these proposals before the directors. Over the vigorous objections of Bard, they authorized Stewart to organize the Union Oil Well Supply Company, a name soon changed to Union Oil Tool Company, and later to Union Tool Company, with Lyman Stewart, W. L. Stewart, J. S. Torrance, and W. A. Carney as directors. Taking over Union Oil's machine shops, stocks, tools, the new company established shops in Los Angeles, Santa Maria, Coalinga, in addition to the one in Santa Paula, dealing in oil-well rigs, casing, tools, engines, and anything else needed in the hunt for more oil. Since no one in the Union shop was an engineer, Lyman Stewart had hired Edward Doble, a bright young Pennsylvanian only twenty years old, on one of his trips East. Doble proved to be a veritable dynamo. When the Union Tool Company was organized, Ed Doble became president and built it into one of the great oil-well supply companies. Doble was only one of a score of Union mechanics, drilling superintendents, and even roustabouts who rose to prominence, several of them becoming millionaires, in the oil business. One, T. A. O'Donnell, eventually became president of the California Petroleum Corporation and American Petroleum Institute.

Outsiders began casting covetous eyes at the growing young oil company. English interests, represented by Mrs. F. F. Lightfoot of New York, offered to buy the company lock, stock, and barrel. Mrs. Lightfoot was given an option for the sale of the company at a price of $3,500,000. Though she carried on negotiations for several months, Mrs. Lightfoot never exercised her option.

Then Standard Oil made a new offer, proposing that it buy all the physical assets of the company. When the directors turned down this proposition, Standard Oil Company in 1898 offered to buy all the stock of the company. By this time Lyman Stewart was unwilling to sell out completely. "I wanted to retain an interest," he explained after the deal fell through. "But Mr. John D. Archibold informed his agent, who was negotiating with us, that they would buy all or none, and that if I wanted an interest in the property I would have to acquire it by purchasing Standard Oil stock."

Stewart and Bard were drifting farther and farther apart. As the eighth annual meeting of stockholders in November, 1898, approached, it was clear that a showdown was impending. Bard started the fireworks by jumping the gun on Stewart in the election of directors of the Sespe Oil Company. He managed to get three out of five directors in this holding company. Bard already had the Torrey Canyon board. With the Hardison interests negligible, this meant Bard held the balance of power on the Union board. Even before the Union directors met, Lyman Stewart realized he had been outsmarted. In the office of R. W. Fenn, the engineer employed to survey Union property, Stewart covered his face with both his hands, saying, "It's all up. I'm a ruined man."

Fenn asked what was the matter. Stew-

111

art explained the trick by which Bard had gotten the drop on him.

"Well, Mr. Bard has forgotten one thing," said Fenn. "He has only two directors on the board of the Torrey Canyon Oil Company. You have two. I am the fifth and deciding man. I will cast my vote for you."

This changed the balance of power on the Union Oil board as well as the Torrey Canyon board. When Bard heard that Fenn had switched to Stewart, he flew into a rage, threatening to wreck the Union Oil Company, and charging Fenn unjustly with having accepted a bribe to support Stewart in the momentous battle.

From this point on, no holds were barred in the battle for control of the company. Bard had one last card up his sleeve. He threatened legal action to force the withdrawal of the Torrey Canyon Oil Company out of the Union Oil Company, on the ground that articles of incorporation of the Torrey Company did not authorize it to hold or vote stock in another corporation. Union had done so much drilling on the Torrey Canyon property at the expense of its other holdings that the Torrey Canyon wells were absolutely essential to Union's business.

Bard's price for calling off the threatened suit was dissolution of all of the holding companies and distribution of Union's stock direct to holders. To avoid a costly suit which he might lose, Stewart agreed, although the dissolution meant that Bard might buy enough stock in the market to gain control of Union Oil Company again. When the new stock was distributed, Stewart and the stockholders he regarded as allies held 50.6 per cent; Bard and his friends owned 39.5 per cent. The Hardisons, no longer actively interested in the company, owned 7.4 per cent. Other stockholders held 2.5 per cent of the stock. Lyman Stewart was boss of Union Oil Company by a margin as thin as the coating of lubricating oil.

The board meeting of November 29, 1898, opened in an atmosphere charged with electric hostility. Bard protested every proposal, including the reelection of Stewart as president. He left in a bitter mood, vowing that it would be Stewart's last meeting as president if any more stock came on the market for sale. He had the money to buy; the Stewarts didn't. Before long Bard was aware that the Stewart faction seemed entirely too sure of themselves for men on the brink of financial disaster. Bard made inquiries. Then he too joined in the financial sleight of hand that led to the battle of men and millions for control of an oil empire.

# CHAPTER SEVEN

# Men after Markets

VIRTUALLY every obstacle that nature, geography, or man could conjure up had to be hurdled before adequate markets prevailed for the vast petroleum resources of California. The oil fields were in Southern California, where less than one-fourth of the state's population lived; the people who needed the oil were in Northern California, where little oil was produced. Avaricious interests reared trade barriers, enacted adverse laws, inflated transportation costs, and generally did everything possible to keep the fledgling Western oil industry from serving the needs of the people of the Pacific slope.

When Lyman Stewart began hunting outlets for oil from Union's wells in the early nineties, the markets were few and far between. The year Union was organized, he persuaded the directors to appropriate $2,500 for a research laboratory, first of its kind in the West. In 1890 this seemed like sheer extravagance. Had anyone suggested then that the day was not far off when Union would spend twice the company's total capitalization in 1890 for a single research center at Brea, it would have seemed fantastic. But the chemical obstinacy of California crude had to be licked before Union's smoking, stinking kerosene could compete with water-white Eastern oils on a quality as well as a price basis. The little research laboratory at Santa Paula was a brave start.

Oil's great competitor in the early nineties was coal. Four out of every five barrels of California crude were sold as fuel. Yet even in the fuel market, the Western oil producers were at a disadvantage. Welsh and Scottish coal, and even Australian coal, was dumped in California as ballast by sailing ships which picked up cargoes of grain and lumber and took them to Europe—and the Antipodes. Though coal was delivered at tidewater at ridiculously low rates, it sold for as much as $30 a ton in the California oil fields as fuel for steam boilers. "The Black Diamond," as coal was known, had one strike

113

against it. The sailing ships arrived irregularly, and neither the coal merchants nor their customers could ever be sure of delivery, a talking point that Lyman Stewart, the oil merchant, was quick to capitalize.

Stewart launched his oil-for-fuel crusade by devising oil burners for the boilers in Union's Santa Paula fields. These worked so well that by the time he moved into the Los Angeles area, he could cite firsthand experience in the use of oil for fuel. Much experimenting had gone into the development of the first "aerated oil burner."

Stewart had tried spreading oil on bricks and on cobblestones to burn it like coal. He had his men saturate wood with oil. Then he hit on the idea of spraying oil into the firebox, eventually mixing it with steam, which improved combustion. By the trial-and-error method, he learned where the burner should be installed in the furnace to give the maximum heat. Stewart encouraged anyone with an idea for making a better oil burner, even inspiring editorial writers to prophesy, as did the editor of a Bakersfield paper:

"The inventive genius of someone will someday confer a benefit on California, where oil for domestic uses is scarce and high priced, by devising a contrivance that will burn crude oil successfully in ordinary stoves. The future burner must act without steam and must be simple and easy to operate."

When he traveled, preaching the gospel of oil, Lyman Stewart invariably carried a satchel containing small sample bottles of petroleum products. To any prospect willing to try oil for fuel, he delivered sample barrels of oil, a practice that met with the hearty disapproval of Thomas R. Bard. Convinced that this was a sheer waste, Bard wanted Union to limit its activities to producing petroleum and delivering oil to merchants, who could develop the markets.

In 1888 Stewart persuaded the builders of a new steamship, the "Pasadena," to install an oil tank on top of the deckhouse from which burners in the furnace were fed by gravity. The oil was atomized by steam. This necessitated a wood and coal fire to start the oil burning. Once the oil was ignited, the wood and coal fire could go out. This was a cumbersome operation, but the owners were pleased with the tests. Their satisfaction was short-lived. Once out at sea, the oil fires went out too because of a surplus of water in the oil. Completely out of steam, the ship wallowed helplessly in the swells until rescued by tug. Stewart had to do some persuasive talking to head off a damage suit and to convince the steamship men that in the future the Santa Paula refinery would deliver more dependable fuel.

Meantime, he had persuaded the owners of the tug "Waterwitch" to convert to oil. An unfortunate explosion forced the temporary abandonment of the craft, giving oil another black eye. Next the ferryboat "Julia," plying between Port Costa and Vallejo, which had been converted to oil burners, suffered an explosion that ripped her apart, killing several people. The steamboat inspectors at San Francisco arbitrarily canceled all permits to use oil as fuel, forcing even the "Pasadena" to switch to coal. The outlook for oil as marine fuel was dark, particularly when the steamboat inspectors refused even to allow Union to use oil as fuel on the company's tanker, the "W. L. Hardison." The combined political influence of Hardison and Bard persuaded authorities in Washington to overrule the local inspectors. Then, to cap the series of misfortunes, the "W. L. Hardison" burned.

Yet by 1902 there were 56 ships on the Pacific Coast using oil as fuel. By perseverance, Stewart had opened up a vast new outlet for Union's products. He celebrated the victory over coal by hanging on the side of the oil-burning tug "Rescue," which the company had chartered to tow barges between Ventura and San Francisco, a huge sign proclaiming, "We Burn Union Oil for Fuel." This was the first advertisement for oil as marine fuel.

Stewart won other converts. Among them was Harrison Grey Otis, publisher of the *Los Angeles Times*. Then, the Los Angeles Tool Company, the Los Angeles City Waterworks, and the Los Angeles Pressed Brick Company installed oil burners. To win these potential customers, he had to give away hundreds of barrels of oil, aggressive selling tactics that earned the hearty disapproval of his associates.

When the Los Angeles Iron and Steel Company was organized, the owners agreed to try oil on two conditions. One was that Union install free burners for the test. The other was that payment for the fuel be made in stock, of which Los Angeles Iron and Steel had plenty, rather than cash of which it had little. Stewart

*Lyman Stewart as he appeared in 1894 when he became president of Union Oil Company.*

agreed. The steel company reported that oil held its fuel costs to half. This convincing testimonial helped sell dozens of other industrialists.

The directors of the Soldiers' Home at Sawtelle and the Whittier State School agreed to try oil for fuel, if Union could wait a year for payment, which had to be approved by the state legislature. The

115

tests were a great success, and eventually the legislature appropriated the funds. In the years that followed, Union sold thousands of barrels of oil to these and other state institutions.

Next, Stewart turned his selling drive on the railroads. The railroaders were harder nuts to crack because they hauled coal from the East and from Utah to California at a big profit. The railroad men not only refused to try oil in their engines, but they hauled coal at lower rates than those charged for moving oil. The locomotives which hauled oil to market used coal.

By the early nineties, Union had become one of the Southern Pacific's big customers. Stewart urged the railroad executives to try oil in just one locomotive. He was turned down cold. Then he tackled E. H. Wade, the general manager of the little Southern California Railway, which later became part of the Santa Fe system. Wade pointed out that his company was small and had no money to spend on experiments. Anyway, he was getting along all right with coal.

"Lend me a locomotive and we'll do the experimenting," said Stewart.

Figuring he had nothing to lose, Wade

*Union Oil bought its first railroad tank car in 1884, shortly after bringing in its first wells. By 1890 the company was operating a fleet of 55 cars under the name of the Mission Transfer Company, a subsidiary. By 1950 Union's fleet totaled 650 cars.*

agreed to send a locomotive to the Union shops at Santa Paula, where Stewart had his mechanics construct an oil tank for the tender. When the tank was finished, Wade tried to call the deal off on the grounds that he couldn't spare a locomotive. Stewart pleaded and cajoled. Weeks later an old and weathered engine puffed painfully onto the spur track of the Union Oil shops in Santa Paula. Though the old engine was about spent, the Union mechanics went to work with enthusiasm, trying first one scheme then another for feeding fuel oil into the firebox. Finally they hit on one that worked. But when the test was made, the locomotive barely managed to move itself along at a snail's pace. The railroad men loaded up with coal and steamed their engine back home.

Undaunted, Stewart and his men went to work on a new burner idea, collaborating with the railroad's mechanics at the San Bernardino shops. Several burners were tested. Eventually one with a flat nozzle that sprayed oil over a wide area was installed forward in the firebox. Came the day in 1894 when the little old locomotive powered by oil was hitched to a string of freight cars and pointed up the hill over Cajon Pass, one of the stiffest railway grades in the country. It pulled the train over the grade without trouble. The railroaders cheered. The Union men cheered. This was the culmination of a dream.

It was a dream that never paid off—for oil man Stewart. The Southern Pacific sent him a bill for $60 for the use of the

*This locomotive was the first in the West to use oil for fuel. In 1894 joint experiments by Union Oil and the Southern California Railway Co. culminated in No. 10 hauling a string of freight cars up Cajon Pass with steam generated by oil instead of coal. (Photo courtesy Santa Fe.)*

*Pacific Steam Whaling and Arctic Oil Works in San Francisco was agent for Union Oil from 1895 to 1904 when Union purchased the whale oil refinery on Potrero Street.*

track over which the engine had been moved from San Bernardino to Santa Paula and back. The Espee chiefs had been watching the experiment, too, and taking advantage of Stewart's demonstration, they converted a number of their engines to oil. But they bought their fuel from Stewart's competitors at cut rates. So did the Santa Fe, which absorbed the Southern California Railway Company. Then both companies developed their own oil fields. The Espee even became a competitor when its executives organized the rival Associated Oil Company. Lyman Stewart had successfully proved that oil was the fuel for Western locomotives, but it brought him no business directly. Indirectly, there was a payoff. The locomotives drank up oil so ravenously that the supply soon ran short and prices rose. The oil that Stewart sold to other industries paid Union a greater profit.

The Western railroads were granting the Standard Oil Company preferential rates, enabling the big Eastern competitor to bring refined products to the Pacific

Coast cheaper than the local producers could deliver them from nearby California oil fields. Stewart became convinced that the railroads were trying to discourage development of Western oil industry. Union's tank cars were often lost or delayed in transit. "Our friends of the Standard are giving us a racket in this business, and we are not yet fully decided as to how to take care of the matter," Lyman Stewart wrote to his brother in Titusville.

After contracting in 1899 for half of the capacity of the Pacific Coast Oil Company's new tanker, which reduced the cost of shipping a barrel of oil from Ventura to San Francisco from 59½ cents charged by the railroad to 4½ cents, Stewart found a brand new market for fuel oil. California was going into beet-sugar production, and the sugar mills were big users of fuel. They had to have mountains of coal or else huge tanks full of oil to tide them over the sugar-processing campaign at the end of each summer. Two big sugar mills agreed to take 200,000 barrels a year for five years from Union, provided the oil could be delivered by tanker to Moss Landing on Monterey Bay. The owners of the new tanker wanted the sugar-mill business, too. The captain of the tanker found it unsafe to go into the ports where Union wanted its oil delivered, and Stewart was advised to forget about selling to the customers in that particular area. Furious at this squeeze, Stewart persuaded Union's directors to build two barges. Towed by tugs, they delivered the fuel.

Stewart's war against his natural enemy, coal, was waged on many fronts. One was the gaslight business. Gas was used for lighting of streets in a number of California cities at the time and also for lighting homes and business buildings. The early gas companies made gas from coal. The San Jose Gas Works had proven that good gas could be made cheaper from petroleum. Capitalizing on this dependable demonstration, Stewart persuaded nearly all the gas companies in the state to convert to oil.

A field in which the California oil men enjoyed a definite advantage was asphalt. The heavy California oil left a residue which made an ideal material for paving roads. While Eastern producers shipped kerosene to the West, selling it cheaper than Western kerosene, Western oil men could beat the Easterners in the asphalt deal. Union opened up a brand new market in 1896 by consigning an entire shipload of asphalt to New York. A solid train of asphalt left Santa Paula for New York in 1897.

The highest grade of asphalt on the market at the time was barreled under Union's Diamond-U brand. Laboratory experiments with this product were beginning to pay off, too. One resulted in a roofing asphalt, which grew into a roofing paper, which in turn gave birth to The Paraffine Companies, Inc., whose Pabco products were a direct offshoot of Union's early experiments. Another by-product was a lampblack used for printing ink and for stove polish.

By the middle nineties, W. L. Hardison was able to report to E. O. Gerberding of Hueneme that the Santa Paula refinery was turning out more than a score of accepted petroleum products. They included gasoline for gas engines, naphtha for use in stoves for heating and domestic use, benzine employed to mix paints and varnishes, distillates used in cooking and heating stoves, still other distillates used by the city gas companies for the enriching of coal gas. Union was also marketing a dozen different types of lubricating oils and greases, seven kinds of asphalts, kerosene, and of course the No. 1 product, fuel oil. By January, 1898, Lyman Stewart could gloat that, "Oil has almost driven steam coal from the market in Los Angeles. Railroads are using it in their locomotives, and all the traction and electric companies and every manufactory use oil exclusively. The demand for this oil

for use as fuel has grown almost as rapidly as the supply, and there is comparatively an inconsiderable surplus at this time."

Stewart was still dreaming up new uses for his oil. He persuaded the electric railways to spray it between rails to lay the dust. He talked road builders into using crude oil, not only to lay the dust but to make the forerunner of asphaltic concrete. He and the petroleum chemists were just beginning to find out what was in a barrel of oil as it flowed out of the oil well. Though Lyman Stewart spearheaded the successful campaign to create markets for petroleum in the West, he never in his wildest dreams realized the extent to which

Union would cash in on the marketing of oil to all the world under the leadership of his son, W. L. Stewart.

The year 1899, when Will Stewart became general manager of Union Oil, ushered in an era of expansion for the Union Oil Company little short of fabulous. Where Lyman Stewart had focused on the California market, Will Stewart reached for global markets. William L. Stewart was the very antithesis of Lyman Stewart. Where Lyman Stewart was devout, precise, and pedantic, Will Stewart was hale, hearty, easy with people, a good mixer in any company. Although both Lyman Stewart and Will Stewart grew up in oil,

Will's training was vastly different from that of his father. Will was born in the shadows of the derricks at Titusville. The early struggles of his father and W. L. Hardison to establish themselves in the West taught him firsthand the vicissitudes, heartaches, and triumphs of the oil game.

It was Will in whom Lyman Stewart confided during the early struggles to put Union on its feet. It was Will who wrote in youthful hand the letters dictated by bedridden Lyman during some of the company's most serious crises. Lyman Stewart saw to it that Will learned the oil business from the oil wells up. While he was a schoolboy in Santa Paula and later

*Los Angeles patrons were served by tank wagons such as this during early part of century.*

*Left: six mule teams once hauled fuel oil and other refined petroleum products to the San Francisco patrons of Union Oil Company. The last horse-drawn vehicle was retired in 1920.*

121

*Serpentlike rubber hoses pour thousands of barrels of oil into tremendous tanks of the "A. C. Rubel," one of the modern tank ships operated by Union Oil Co. This ship has a capacity of 100,000 barrels and can be loaded or discharged in a single day.*

in Los Angeles, Will worked at jobs around the company's properties. While a student at the University of California, Will Stewart spent his summers with the rig builders in the field. His full-time duties began in 1894. He liked working with the field men. They liked to have him around. Although Lyman Stewart would have been horrified, Will learned to smoke, chew, and drink with the field men. He was one of their kind.

This training paid off for Will Stewart and for the company. By 1898 it was apparent that the pressure of double duty as president and general manager was too much for Lyman Stewart. Will Stewart was secretary of Union, and he knew more about the company's manifold activities than anyone else, including, probably, his father. On December 13, 1898, the directors promoted him to general manager at a salary of $300 per month. The appointment was vehemently protested by Bard, who became so angry that he resigned his directorship in protest. It was characteristic of Will Stewart's directness that he talked things out with Bard and persuaded him to hold the resignation "in abeyance." Before a year had passed, Bard moved that "our general manager's salary be increased to $375, as he is working very hard and spending his whole strength in the interests of the corporation." The directors went even farther. They made Will Stewart vice-president as well.

Will Stewart was instrumental, in 1899,

The "Santa Paula," a full-rigged schooner with a capacity of 8,200 barrels, was the second tank ship operated by Union Oil. She made her maiden voyage to Honolulu in 1900, the first time Union made an offshore delivery on its own ship. Eventually she became a barge.

*Hauling boilers across the desert for pumping stations on the Producers' Pipe Line from San Joaquin valley to the sea was part of building the 240 miles of 8-inch line in record time. The $4,500,000 line carried 30,000 barrels a day to San Luis Obpiso.*

*C. B. Kibele (black hat), chief engineer during laying of Producers' Pipe Line, uses one of company's first automobiles to make inspection of line over desert and mountains.*

in persuading John Baker, Jr., to head the company's San Francisco branch, with responsibility for the refinery at Oleum. Oleum had been losing so much that the directors seriously considered selling or leasing the refinery. Will Stewart and John Baker changed that. They became a sales team which drove ahead so fast that within five years Union was selling in Alaska, South America, Hawaii, and Central America. Where Lyman Stewart had laid a firm foundation in the company's own back yard, Will Stewart and John Baker launched a great tanker fleet, developed a 700-mile pipeline system, invaded the Eastern seaboard to challenge the big oil trusts in their home grounds. Their aggressive selling campaigns soon were felt in every department of the company. It was felt by the directors and the stockholders, too.

By 1900 there was terrific overproduction of oil, particularly from the new fields at Coalinga, Kern River, Los Angeles, Brea. The West Coast oil industry was in an economic slump, swamped by a flood of petroleum. Will Stewart and John Baker put their heads together and came up with what they called the "Off-Shore Sales Program." The kickoff came in January, 1901, when Will Stewart persuaded the board that Union was overlooking a potentially profitable business in the Hawaiian Islands.

John Baker was sent to Hawaii, where he bumped head-on into Lyman Stewart's old nemesis, coal. The plantation owners imported thousands of tons of coal to make steam for their sugar mills. Vessels plying the lumber trade between the Pacific Northwest and Australia brought coal from Australia to Hawaii at low rates, unloading it there and taking on rock ballast for the balance of the trip to Seattle. Baker persuaded three large sugar mills to switch to oil. By 1903 the Hawaiian trade had reached such huge proportions that it was an eye opener for Union's ambitious second generation.

With fuel sales growing in Hawaii and Alaska as well, Will Stewart and John Baker decided the world was their oyster. Baker was assigned to cover first Central and South America, then Europe, peddling California's liquid black gold. In one year he traveled 50,000 miles marketing oil. A remarkable and exuberant personality,

Baker doubled the sale of asphalt in the New York area, and even persuaded dealers along the Atlantic Coast to handle Union's other refinery products. He sold so much oil that Union's directors were forced to buy four first-class steamers and lease two others to fill the orders.

Baker's sales expeditions had their humorous side. To get big orders quickly, he entertained lavishly. The Union accountants, accustomed to the modest expense accounts turned in by Lyman Stewart, scrutinized Johnnie Baker's "swindle sheets" and gasped. When a clerk showed one of them to Lyman Stewart he too was speechless over such items as wine and cigars. Lyman Stewart took the matter up with the executive committee, which "disapproved the charges made against the company for wine, cigars, and extravagant hostelry expenditures properly belonging only on the personal accounts of employes." It ordered the accounting department to withhold payment on any "unseemly figures not in the interests of stockholders."

Will Stewart was absent when this resolution passed. When he heard about it, he voiced his opposition so emphatically that the executive committee, including Lyman Stewart, reversed the order at the next meeting, authorizing the auditor to "pass items in reasonable amounts" covering "telegrams, telephone, cablegrams, porter tips, waiter tips, bellboy tips, cab hire, baggage transfer, laundry bill, theater and entertainment, tickets, dinners (with the names of parties entertained)."

Nothing was too big for John Baker to try. President Theodore Roosevelt had just worked out the tremendous project of building the Panama Canal. Baker and Will Stewart hit on the idea of a pipeline across the Isthmus of Panama. On his next Eastern trip, Baker dropped in at the White House to talk pipelines with "T. R." The President heartily supported the idea and promised that Union could build it. Later, when large and powerful Eastern interests tried to win the concession, "T. R." stood by his word. He gave the permit to the upstart young Western company to build the line along the Panama Railway's right of way. By the end of 1906 the line was finished. Though the pipeline proved useful in supplying the canal builders with oil, new oil fields in South America and Texas made it uneconomical to pump California oil to the Atlantic. The Panama pipeline was spectacular, but only three tankers of oil, about 150,000 barrels, were pumped from ocean to ocean.

Though Union's business mushroomed fantastically, Baker and Will Stewart had still bigger ideas. In 1908 they spent $140,000 on 78 acres of land at South Chester, near Philadelphia, to build a refinery for the production of asphalt and distillate. The refinery was never completed because Eastern sales outlets agreed to handle Union's products. By this time Baker had established depots in

*Union Oil pipeline between Bakersfield and San Luis Obispo cuts straight across the hills.*

Central America and in Chile. While Baker was traveling south and east, Will Stewart covered Japan, China, and other potential markets across the Pacific. The expedition bore fruit in the sale of millions of barrels of petroleum products in the Orient at a later date.

Union's business was growing so fast that it almost foundered the company. Salesmen like Baker could sell the oil in enormous quantities. Union's drillers proved in Lompoc, Santa Maria, and Coalinga that they could produce it. The capacity of the Oleum refinery was stepped up fivefold, and the smaller Bakersfield plant, which had been built in 1902, was running to capacity. But neither the pipelines nor the available tankers could boost their capacity to handle the loads.

Despite the plethora of business, the year 1906 was a disastrous one for Union. In the rush to deliver building materials to the Oleum refinery, the steamship "Santa Rita" on her maiden voyage from an Eastern shipyard sailed with a cargo not properly secured. It shifted in a storm and had to be jettisoned. Gas explosions caused four fires in Union oil fields. At Portsmouth, Oregon, an employee used a lantern instead of an electric torch to check a storage tank. The resulting explosion killed him and wrecked the plant. The earthquake and fire that destroyed San Francisco deprived the refinery of much needed materials for enlargement. Four freighters converted into tankers were so poorly constructed that the vessels were out of service for weeks at a time. A strike by shipyard workers delayed the delivery of another tanker eight

*Gleaming wax comes from black crude at Oleum Refinery and is sold as Aristowax.*

months. Still another tanker hit a bar in the Columbia River and burst into flames. As usual, the company was broke, and it was next to impossible to get money in the depressed market.

But Union's assets were imposing. The company had 188,000 acres of oil territory. It had 171 highly productive wells, 200 miles of trunk and feeder pipelines, seven tankers, three of them with a capacity in excess of 50,000 barrels. The company was spending around $325,000 a year for new wells and other facilities. The Oleum refinery had stepped up its capacity to 5,000 barrels a day.

In the fast-expanding San Joaquin Valley oil fields and in Los Angeles, a new development destined to be a major factor in the future of the Union Oil Company was in the making. For several years producers who later organized the Independent Oil Producers Agency, an association

*William Lyman Stewart, fourth president of Union Oil, served from April, 1914, until his sudden death in June, 1930. He worked for thirty-six years in various capacities.*

of 150 small companies, had been delivering oil to the Standard Oil Company and to the Associated Oil Company. In 1909–1910 when production increased from 52 million to 77 million barrels, with a consequent demoralization of prices, neither Standard nor Associated would give the producers what they thought they should have for their oil.

Spokesmen for the independents, long on friendly terms with Union executives, both in the field and in the marketing department, came to Union in 1909 with a proposition. Would Union act as sales agent for the smaller independent producers? A ten-year agreement was reached whereby Union undertook to handle all the oil of the Producers Agency, guaranteeing them the same price that Union got for its own products. This vast river of oil, doubling the amount that Union had to market, was snatched away from Associated Oil Company, owned by Southern Pacific, and from Standard Oil Company. Most of it came from the San Joaquin Valley fields where Union had been unable to match the two big competitors because of the high cost of rail transportation.

To move the oil from the San Joaquin Valley fields to the sea, Union Oil Company and the Producers Agency jointly organized the Producers Transportation Company, which rushed construction of an 8-inch pipeline from the Valley oil fields to tidewater at Port Harford in San Luis Obispo County, later known as Avila. At the time it was a colossal pipeline project, calling for 240 miles of pipe, 15 pumping stations, steel tankage to store 27 million barrels of oil, plus the wharf facilities at Port Harford. It was an expensive project. Before Union and the Agency members had finished it, they had spent $4,500,000, a million more than had been estimated.

"We were in a tremendous hurry," Will Stewart said, by way of explaining the great cost. The first pipe was laid on July

*The great TCC Unit (Thermofor Catalytic Cracking) at the Los Angeles refinery is seen for miles at night as it towers 268 feet (22 stories) above the ground.*

29, 1909, and the first oil was delivered at Port Harford the following March. In one respect the pipeline exceeded all expectations. It was planned with a 20,000-barrel-a-day capacity. But when the pumps began pushing, they drove more than 30,000 barrels a day over the hills to the sea.

During the ensuing years, as various stockholders in the Producers Transportation Company wished to dispose of holdings in the company, Union bought them in. Eighteen years after the line was completed, the company owned all of the stock, and Producers became an integral part of the Union pipeline network.

By 1914, when the time had come for the younger generation to take over the Union helm, two men were headed for the one presidency—William L. Stewart and John Baker, Jr. When the board chose Stewart, Baker resigned. After an extended visit to Europe, he launched an asphalt business in Chicago. Two years later the dapper little supersalesman was back in California organizing a syndicate, with several former associates among his many partners, to deal in oil lands and leases, an oil-hunting venture which lacked the flare and success Baker had introduced so spectacularly to oil marketing.

As Will Stewart stepped into the president's shoes in April, 1914, replacing his father who became chairman of the board, Union had 328 wells in operation; its 226,000 acres of oil lands were valued at $22,776,000; its fleet had grown to eleven steamers and six chartered vessels, with a total carrying capacity of 800,000 barrels; its pipeline system had grown to 600 miles; its storage system could handle 7 million barrels; sales had climbed to 20 million dollars a year.

"The Union Oil Company as it stands today is one of the most remarkable achievements in the history of the petroleum industry in this or any country," wrote H. S. Reabus, the publisher of the *Oil Trade Journal*. It appeared that Union had reached its zenith. Actually, the young giant of a company was just beginning to flex its muscles.

# CHAPTER EIGHT

# Of Gushers, Dusters, and Gassers

SINCE Lyman Stewart and Wallace Hardison made their inauspicious start with seven dry holes in a row, Union's drillers have punched more than eight thousand wells, all the way from below the Equator to the Arctic Circle, in the never-ending hunt for oil. One out of every four holes has been a "duster," commercially worthless. At the other extreme, Union's crews have drilled some of the most prodigious producers, including one fabulous well that gushed 9 million barrels of oil in eighteen months, the mightiest gusher in petroleum history.

"The successful driller is the one whose producers outnumber his dry holes by one," wryly comments A. C. "Cy" Rubel, vice-president in charge of exploration and production.

Oil wells, big or little, producers or dusters, are designated by name of the field and number, such as Adams No. 28, Union's first gusher, or Lake View No. 1, the company's and the world's greatest gusher. But every now and then a hole

in the ground develops a personality, for no particular reason, and the drilling crews honor it with a nickname.

Hartnell No. 1 in the Santa Maria field was that sort of a well. This spectacular hole in the ground was an oil well with a story from the start. Oil men began calling the well "Old Maud" soon after she was spudded in. Old Maud was a lucky mistake. Had she been located where she was supposed to be drilled, Old Maud would have been just another number in the oil-well records. Jack Reed, later drilling superintendent for Union Oil, a member of the crew which brought in Old Maud, tells why.

"We really caught it from the boss after we started drilling," he said. "Back in those days, 1904, nobody thought a few feet one way or the other made much difference. The boss told our rigging crew to put the enginehouse here and the derrick there. Well, it was a hot day, and when the boiler accidentally fell off the wagon where the derrick should have

131

*Noted oddities among Western wells are Hartnell No. 1 (left) and Hartnell No. 7 in the Santa Maria field. Hartnell No. 1 was drilled by mistake and produced 3,000,000 barrels as a gusher. Hartnell No. 7, only 65 feet away, never produced more than 250 barrels a day.*

been, we left it right there and put up the derrick where the enginehouse should have been. The boss was hopping mad, but not quite mad enough to make us tear down a whole day's work and start over again.

"That was our good luck. We spudded in June 22, 1904, and on December 2, when no one was expecting much of a well, Old Maud suddenly starts rumbling. Then with a roar, a column of oil and gas shoots up through the rig floor to a height of 150 feet. Oil begins pouring down the gullies and creek beds. We have the biggest producer the world has ever seen. We can't control it, what with 12,-000 barrels of oil pouring out every day. We don't even have tanks or pipelines big enough to handle the flow, so we scrape up a series of earth dams. Pools of crude collect for miles below as the flow continues day after day for three months."

"Yeah, and by mistake one of the workmen closed a valve," cut in Frank Hill, who was superintendent on the job.

*Hartnell No. 1, called "Old Maud" by the Union Oil crew that drilled her, came in for 12,000 barrels a day on December 2, 1904, and was world's greatest gusher at the time.*

*Two views of modern cycling plant at South Coles Levee field. Here natural gasoline and other products are extracted from gas and the remaining gas pushed back underground to bring up still more gasoline. This is an endless cycle, hence the plant's name.*

"This completely shuts in the well which is under great gas pressure. This starts the oil flowing through the formations, and for hundreds of yards around every squirrel and gopher hole begins to spout oil. The surrounding fields are full of miniature geysers of oil. We finally get the valve opened and the pressure released. The oil begins spurting through the casing again instead of the squirrel holes."

Petroleum engineers, who came to scoff, excitedly measured the flow in weir boxes, and found the 12,000-barrels-a-day figure to be correct. In the first one hundred days Old Maud yielded 1 million barrels. The well flowed for over two years and yielded nearly 3 million barrels before being put on the pump.

"Everybody in the neighborhood comes to see Old Maud, and we have our job cut out for us keeping visitors from tossing cigar butts or lighted matches into the streams and reservoirs of oil," continued Reed. "One night a train crew from the Pacific Coast Railway comes over to take a look. Each man carries a lighted kerosene lantern. We find the railroaders bending down close to the oil to get a good look. It is just good luck that Old Maud doesn't go up in smoke."

Even so spectacular a well failed to excite Lyman Stewart unduly.

"When I heard of Old Maud's tremendous yield I phoned Frank Garbutt, our field manager," recalled Frank Hill. "He asked what I figured the well would make. I told him 10,000 barrels a day. He yelled, 'Spell it out; it sounded like you said 10,000 barrels.' So I spelled it out for him.

"Garbutt next called Will Stewart and told him we had a 10,000-barrel producer. Will also asked that the figure be spelled out and commented, 'It's a good story, anyway, and a good job of drilling in any man's language.' Will phoned his father, who asked, 'Did you say 10,000 barrels? Spell it out.' So for the fourth time that night we 'spelled it out' over the phone.

"Lyman Stewart merely said, 'Thank you. I have been expecting something big from up there. Good night.'"

Old Maud continued producing for fourteen years, and even then was good for 250 barrels a day. One day in 1918 the 8-inch casing collapsed. Since it looked like an expensive job to fish the tubing and rods out of the hole, the field men decided to drill a twin well nearby, to be known as Hartnell No. 7. Hartnell No. 7 was located 65 feet away, on the exact spot where they had been told to put the first Hartnell derrick in 1904. Hartnell No. 7 produced only 95 barrels on its best day.

*Dehydration plant in Cat Canyon plays important part in getting petroleum from wells to refineries. Here water is removed before the crude is sent to the pipeline enroute to storage.*

Old Maud, like the proverbial cat, had many lives. In 1943 when the wartime demand for more and more oil became critical, the field superintendent decided to clean out the well and see if Maud wouldn't produce again. A crew succeeded in yanking out 1,765 feet of tubing and rods, a working barrel, a joint of anchor, some chain tongs, and pieces of practically everything that was ever fished out of a well. When a new pump was installed, Old Maud yielded 175 barrels a day, once more becoming one of the field's top producers.

Hitting a gusher, of course, is a rare

experience. Hundreds of drillers spend their lives without ever being on hand when one comes in. Charlie Wood, one of the early day Union drillers, had even worse luck—he didn't even hit a producing well of any description for so many years that he earned the distinctive, if unflattering, cognomen of "Dry Hole Charlie." Year after year Charlie drilled nothing but dusters. He drilled seven consecutive dry holes for A. P. Johnson near Newhall and punched down eight more holes for Graham & Loftus at Gilroy without a sign of oil, all in one year.

Figuring he had a jinx in California, he

struck out for other fields. He did no
better away from home. Charlie returned
and drilled a well 4,500 feet for Union
at San Juan Capistrano. It was the inevitable duster. Then he was sent to the
Summers field at Gardena, where he went
down 5,000 feet. Another dry hole. Next
he put down the bone-dry Francis No. 1
on the Dominguez Rancho.

Wood was a good driller, and where
an especially difficult job had to be wildcatted in a lonely spot on top of the hills
miles away from supplies, Charlie was
the man for the job. He was a specialist
on wildcatting. The brevity of his reports
was impressive. They invariably read, "It
was a dry hole."

After Dry Hole Charlie had drilled
dusters in just about every field the company was prospecting, his big moment
came, up on Union's Sage & Webster lease
in the San Joaquin Valley. This was early
in 1908. Nearby, four partners with a
big hunch and a little capital held a lease
alongside the road between Taft and
Maricopa. The quartet, Charles W. Off,
Julius Fried, Parker Barrett, and John M.
Dunn, called their operation The Lake
View Oil Company. They encountered
hard luck from the start, but no more so
than hundreds of others. Two of the
partners were rig builders. By erecting
their own 72-foot derrick, they were able
to start drilling on a shoestring. But soon
after they began to make hole, the bit
wandered off at a bad angle. They had
enough cash between them to buy only
one string of tools. When the cable broke
and their tools vanished down the hole,
they came over to beg or borrow fishing
equipment from the nearby Union crew.

*Injection well sends water underground to
wash sands free of crude. This is known as
the "water flooding" method of oil recovery.*

137

LAKE VIEW NO.1

*World's greatest oil well, Lake View No. 1, hurling stream of oil two feet in diameter with such force it tore huge hole in earth.*

*Charles (Dry Hole Charlie) Wood one day saw reputation spoiled by tremendous gusher.*

After fishing for days, they hooked their missing tools and started to bring them up. Then the cable parted again. Everything was lost—tools and fishing equipment alike.

Up against it, the partners asked Union for more help. The company loaned them C. E. "Barney" Barnhart, one of Union's most experienced drillers. He retrieved the lost tools and began to drill again. Then, at 1,800 feet, the partners ran completely out of resources. The hole was not deep enough to be conclusive, but far too deep to be forgotten. They asked Union to take over. Already occupied with several wildcatting operations, none of them showing much promise, the company didn't want another. However, to help the unfortunate quartet, Union's exploration department agreed to complete the well in spare time, if and when drilling crews were idle. Though the partners were willing to sell their lease cheap, Union took only 51 per cent of it. The four wildcatters kept 49 per cent.

Barnhart continued as superintendent, with Dry Hole Charlie as foreman on the job. No one expected much from the hole. During odd hours the well finally was punched down to 2,200 feet. Union's

nearby Sage Lease test well had priority on all drilling. The Sage well sanded up the night of March 14, 1910, so when the midnight tour reported for duty, the men were told to go on over to the Lake View job and do some drilling.

Two hours later they pulled the bailer from the bottom of Lake View's 2,200-foot hole. To their surprise they found it dripping with oil. They hurriedly dropped it again and again, and each time it struck oil at a higher level. Here, in the darkness, was a gusher a-borning! By dawn March 15, water, shale, and sand began burbling and tumbling out of the well. Just as Dry Hole Charlie came on the job at 8 A.M., a column of gas and oil roared hundreds of feet high, drenching all the surrounding area with petroleum.

Hour by hour the roaring increased and the tremendous stream doubled and redoubled in size. It grew stronger and stronger, blasting out a crater so deep and wide that the derrick and all the drilling equipment disappeared. No one knew how to cap such a terrific geyser of oil. Dams were hurriedly thrown up to catch the Black Bonanza, which by this time was a greater flood than oil men had ever seen, surpassing even Hartnell No. 1.

139

Dry Hole Charlie was dancing like an Indian. "Gosh, we've cut an artery down there," he yelled.

Calling every man in the area to help, Charlie Wood and his crew frantically piled sandbags to throw temporary reservoirs around the well. They were filled and overflowing in no time. Wood sent out a desperate call for help. Hundreds of men responded. They worked hour after hour, in clothing drenched with oil which was raining down over several acres of area.

The gusher roared on. Crews moved down the hill and tossed up a giant reservoir called The Cornfield, covering 16 acres. They were just finishing work on this huge basin when an earthquake shook apart the walls of the first sumps they had built. The oil came rushing down into The Cornfield.

For months the well spouted completely out of control. It was estimated that 125,000 barrels of petroleum were hurled out the first twenty-four hours. Thirty days after the first gush, the flow was gauged by engineers at 90,000 barrels a day. For months after that its daily production remained constant at 50,000 barrels a day.

*Rio Bravo absorption plant operated by Union Oil under unitization program with three other companies. Natural gasoline and raw liquid petroleum are first extracted and from the remaining gas propane, isobutane and normal butane are removed before the "dry" gas is ultimately used for fuel or forced underground to maintain field pressure.*

*When wells get clogged with sand or other foreign material they are cleaned out by pulling thousands of feet of sucker rods from the well before swabbing it out. Portable steel derricks such as this one are wheeled into position with speed when wells choke.*

From The Cornfield a 2-mile long 4-inch pipeline, leading to eight 55,000-barrel tanks, was installed in the amazing time of only four hours. Never had a line been laid so fast or under such desperate circumstances. These tanks relentlessly filled while crews rushed the new 8-inch Producers pipeline to Avila on the coast.

"What we feared most," recalled Dry Hole Charlie, "was an early rain. A flash flood could have spread our ocean of oil down over the valley below. So we went up into the hills with an army of 600 men and dammed up the mouths of canyons with earth walls 20 feet high and 50 feet thick. Down below we built storage for 10 million barrels of oil. We used 9 million barrels of this capacity before the Lake View gusher calmed down."

Lake View's torrential flood of oil hit the market like a sledge hammer. Petroleum prices were driven down day after day as the gusher kept on roaring. Crude oil fell to 30 cents a barrel. Preachers conducted excursions to the spot, exhorting people to pray that the oil might not cover the world and bring flaming destruction. That Lake View did not catch fire was a miracle.

On September 9, 1911, after eighteen

141

*Glory fades rapidly. All that remains of world's greatest oil well is this debris.*

months of stupendous production, Lake View ceased gushing as abruptly as it was born. The hole caved in. Two years later, when Union redrilled the well, it yielded only 35 barrels a day on the pump. Official estimates of Lake View's yield were 9 million barrels of 32-gravity crude. Five million barrels of this were saved, the remainder was lost by evaporation and seepage.

Though Union had struck the richest oil well of all times, there were days when the company's executives wished it were somebody else's lucky strike. The oil came from the well in a solid stream 2 feet or more in diameter and spewed 200 feet skyward. The spray covered an area 15 miles away from the well, ruined clothes, covered machinery, vehicles, and buildings and provoked many lawsuits from adjoining property owners. The flood of crude drove the oil price to an unprofitable low. As for Dry Hole Charlie, he had seen his luck change. He had bossed the drilling of the greatest producer in history. So he went right out and drilled a dozen more wells, nearly all of them bone-dry!

The career of Dry Hole Charlie about covers the field—a record producer of both dust and oil. Thrills and heartaches. Gushers and wells that ran "wild," such as Old Maud and Lake View No. 1, are spectacular and exciting. However, they are so wasteful of precious petroleum and gas that such a well today would be considered a disgrace. The modern oil producer brings in a well under complete control. The chances are few that more oil gushers will be seen in this country, because as a modern well nears produc-

*One little engine operating on natural gas furnishes power for pumping two Union Oil wells in Tar Creek field. Ingenious use of connecting cable permits wells to work simultaneously, as every stroke of Well 49 pulls the line and causes pump on background well to move also.*

tion, the crew gets set to keep the initial flow under control by means of a complicated and ingenious system of fittings and valves attached to the casing and known as the "Christmas Tree." Each Christmas Tree is individually designed for the well upon which it is used—the number of valves and their sizes are figured out scientifically on the basis of estimated gas and oil production from the well.

When oil or gas reaches the surface under control of the Christmas Tree, it is piped into storage tanks or pipelines. Its flow can be reduced or entirely shut off with a twist of the valve wheels. Today, oil men would rather bring in a controlled producer averaging a dozen or a score or a hundred barrels a day than the most exciting gusher.

It is doubtful if any gusher was better timed than the one brought in by a Union crew in Mexico in 1921, during a critical shortage of fuel oil and refined products in the Western states. The company had been forced to import large quantities of crude oil and gasoline to meet domestic demands and had to cease exporting refined products. Fuel-oil contracts in Chile and other South American points were in jeopardy. Union had turned down three huge and profitable export orders, aggregating 15 million gallons of kerosene at a 3-cents-per-gallon premium. It had practically canceled its offshore trade. In common with every other producer, the company was figuratively behind the eight ball. At the time Union had forty rigs at work around the clock, making hole in all available domestic fields, and though they had brought in 44 new producers

*Santa Maria field wells produce excessive amounts of carbon dioxide, so Union Oil uses this plant to extract the $CO_2$ and turn it into dry ice to refrigerate cars of California fruits en route east. Natural gasoline is also extracted from gas produced in this area.*

good for 8,800 barrels a day, it was not enough to supply the South American trade which the company had so carefully nurtured. Then President W. L. Stewart persuaded the Mexican government into permitting Union drillers to wildcat in the Tampico area, near Mexico City. Nobody was placing any bets on the drilling crew dispatched to Mexico when a brief bulletin flashed over the wires from George G. Hunt, in charge of Union's Tampico office. It read: "Well on Lot 114 came in clean at 7:30 this morning, the largest well in the field. Estimate of 80,000 barrels a day is ultra conservative. . . ."

This well, plus one other, gushed 4 million barrels of high-grade oil between July and December—enough to permit the company to meet its contractual obligations in Central and South America and to ease the strain on the domestic market. Then, like the climax of a drama, these wells, which had suddenly burst into production when oil was so urgently needed, ceased to produce. By the close of the year, the pumps were running dry. No wells in all Union's history, aside from Star No. 1, the original producer that launched Stewart and Hardison in business, were more timely and welcome than these holes south of the border.

While some of Union's drillers were seeking oil in the Mexican sunshine, others were battling the wintry cold of Wyoming, where well sites were often buried deep under snowdrifts, to find oil to relieve the shortage.

"I left the Manville Station at 7:30 A.M. in a very mild snowstorm and headed for the Harris-Baker well site," C. H. Sherman, Union's manager in Wyoming, reported. "The trip was made through 12 inches of snow, and we drove the 22 miles in two and a half hours. We left the rig at ten o'clock the same night, and about 4 miles from the well threw the left front wheel of the car. After groping around in the snow, we tried to put it back on and thought we had successfully done so. A quarter of a mile farther on, however, the same wheel went out across the prairie and we could not find it. The weather had changed very quickly, and we were now caught out in the open in a real Wyoming blizzard. We were nearly frozen. About midnight we stumbled into a ranchhouse, built a fire and stayed for the night. We went through the blizzard the next morning, found our wheel, put

*"Christmas Trees" control flow of oil and gas through arrangement of valves, pipes and dials tailored to needs of the individual well.*

145

*To determine pressures in oil wells a long "bomb" filled with precision instruments is lowered and foot-by-foot "picture" recorded.*

it on, shoveled snow all the way to Manville, arriving there at six o'clock in the evening."

That such wintertime experiences were somewhat routine was indicated by another report the same winter in which Sherman said, "I have picked up on the road a number of men with their feet frozen. In many instances they started out on trucks bound for the oil fields, had gone 8 or 10 miles before being overtaken by a blizzard. The drivers were compelled to break down posts along the road and build fires to keep from freezing.

146

Frequently it has taken them five hours to drive ten miles."

Union drillers brought in their share of discovery wells in major oil fields, including Santa Paula, Salt Marsh, Bardsdale, Sespe, Topo, Torrey, Conejo, Sisar Creek, Lompoc, Santa Maria Valley, Dominguez, Richfield, Rosecrans-Athens, Santa Fe Springs, Brea Canyon, and Rio Bravo. In one five-year period, beginning in 1919, Union oil wildcatters discovered four of Southern California's major fields —Richfield, Santa Fe Springs, Dominguez, and Rosecrans.

In 1901 oil experts and scientists made a comprehensive survey of California's reserves and solemnly warned that all the oil in the state would be gone by 1912. The wasteful, extravagant methods of producing oil at the time might well have caused concern. There was little effort to conserve. So little was really known about the subterranean make-up of the oil fields that the wonder is not that so much oil and gas were wasted but that oil men managed to recover as much as they did.

Early-day operators in California considered gas to be a nuisance and released it into the air. Likewise, they believed erroneously that the more sand a well threw up the better the well, reasoning that this sand meant a large cavity was being dug at the bottom of the well, making a natural reservoir from which they could pump clean oil. The policy of the early driller was to have his well throw as much sand as possible and release the gas as rapidly as it could be blown to the four winds.

Some wells known as "gassers" produce no oil at all, yielding only gas. Of these

*Gas traps must continue to function perfectly regardless of weather, so, despite bitter cold of 20 to 30 degrees below zero, Union Oil employees keep dials and pipes clear on company's field operations near Cut Bank, Montana.*

Union has had its share. A typical gasser was Union's Community Well No. 11 at Long Beach, which began roaring at 9 A.M. July 10, 1923. Chunks of rock and a stream of sand were hurled 100 feet into the air as a flow of gas estimated at 50 million cubic feet a day burst out of the hole. After six days the well sanded up without catching fire, although paradoxically a bonfire was burning close by when the gasser started. Drilling crews risked their lives to put out the fire. This gas was worth upwards of $15,000 a day, even by values at that time when crude oil was selling for only 90 cents a barrel. This gasser was a blowout of shallow gas with water and could not have been developed commercially.

An even more spectacular gasser was Union's Alexander No. 1 in the Santa Fe Springs field, which blew for twenty-nine days, destroying the rig within the first three minutes and blasting out a huge crater around the well. A driller saw the mud starting to boil over the rotary table, and yelled to the derrickman, working 75 feet above the ground, to get down and fast. Before the derrickman could scram-

147

*Richest oil shale outcroppings in Colorado have been owned by Union Oil since 1921.*

ble down, the well exploded, sending a huge column of mud, rocks, and gas through the derrick. The 900 feet of 8-inch pipe, in the hole at the time the blowout started, went through the derrick 200 feet up into the air and plunged into the earth 700 feet away. The bit and drill collar were completely embedded in the ground. During this blast, the derrickman leaped 50 feet to the ground, hit a mud hole, and miraculously escaped unhurt. It took a month to get control of this monster gasser.

Gas wells in California are as old as oil wells. Natural gas was discovered at

Stockton around 1864 when wells being drilled for water yielded gas instead. This gas was captured for manufacturing and domestic purposes. The first productive oil and gas well was completed in Pico Canyon, near Newhall, in 1870. As early as 1885 the Standard Gaslight and Fuel Company had been formed at Merced to develop natural gas in the San Joaquin Valley.

Since 1909, when large-volume, high-pressure gas wells were drilled in the Buena Vista hills, Kern County, and high-pressure separators or gas traps were first installed, the proportion of gas saved has gradually reversed from complete wastage to practically complete utilization. Now millions of Californians are using this natural gas. One of the first utility companies to serve its customers with straight natural gas was the Santa Maria Gas Company, organized in 1907. During 1913 and 1914 gas was piped from the San Joaquin fields to the Los Angeles area, where it was mixed with an artificial gas to lower the B.t.u. rating and make it safer to use. By 1927 all of the Los Angeles Basin area was served with 100 per cent natural gas. In 1929 natural gas reached San Francisco from the Kettleman Hills area. By 1940 nearly every important community in California was served with natural gas.

Early drilling and production methods merely skimmed the cream of the oil

*Future of oil industry may be contained in this little retort developed by Union Oil to extract oil from shale. Retort generates own heat, uses no water, and is virtually "self-supporting." Union has also found a method of removing nitrogen and sulphur from shale oil so that the product can be refined with existing equipment and processes.*

148

149

fields, figuratively speaking, recovering as little as 10 per cent of the oil in the natural reservoirs below the surface of the earth. Even with all the techniques and knowledge of nearly a century of production, probably not more than a quarter of the petroleum is recovered. An oil field may be likened to a great underground storage tank of sands permeated with oil held under pressure created by gas or water, singly or in combination. This pressure provides the "drive" for forcing the oil to flow through the sands to the oil well, which is a hole punched into the top of the "tank." The pressure pushes the oil or gas up the hole. If the pressure is dissipated, a large amount of the remaining oil is locked in the sands of the underground reservoir. Oil is lazy stuff. Unless something gives it a push, it lies dormant.

Generations of oil men have dreamed of schemes of giving the lazy oil trapped in the sands an artificial push. An accidental flooding of some of the wells in the Bradford, Pennsylvania, field in 1907, resulting in a startling increase in production from old wells, started them experimenting with "lifting," as this secondary recovery is known, both by "water drive" and "gas drive."

Union oil hunters have been among these dreamers. Probably the first demonstration of the "gas-lift" technique in the West was in 1911, when Union increased

Bell No. 6 in Cat Canyon, Santa Barbara County, from 100 barrels a day to 5,000, by pumping in millions of cubic feet of gas. This was spectacular recovery. Unfortunately neither Union nor any other operator has been able to duplicate it. But "gas lifting" has paid off in many fields, particularly since Phillip Jones of Santa Maria, California, developed and patented the process for forcing compressed gas into wells to activate the sluggish trapped petroleum, extracting the gasoline from the gas, compressing the latter and pushing it down the well again. More recently, experimenters have found that hydrocarbon gas, forced into wells under high pressure, will recover even greater percentages of the lost oil.

The "water drive" was pioneered by Union in the prodigious Richfield field in Southern California, where natural pressure was negligible in most wells. After the field had yielded some 36 million barrels of crude, engineers concluded that only a few more million barrels could be recovered by routine pumping. But they had a hunch that there were quantities of dormant oil trapped in the sands and decided to force the oil out with water. The hunch paid off fantastically. A quarter of a century later, after they had lifted out 195 million barrels of crude, they were still pumping in water and pumping out more oil.

During the early years of the industry,

*Spectacular blowout of a gasser—Alexander No. 2 in the Santa Fe Springs field—resulted in little actual loss. The well was not on fire—yet—but two minutes after picture was taken flames broke out at bottom of derrick and spread upward. What appear to be clouds of smoke and flame are actually billows of gas, sand, and oil. Fire was controlled in few hours.*

150

the prevailing idea was to pump out as much oil as possible as fast as possible. In time, oil men learned that a more efficient system was to draw the oil out at a rate which yielded the most barrels with the least loss of underground pressure. Lyman Stewart put this theory into practice long before it was proved scientifically, withdrawing only from 2 to 4 per cent of the estimated resources of a field. His long field experience convinced him that it paid in the long run to conserve petroleum in natural storage. As the result of this shrewd policy, many of the fields he first brought into production are still profitable producers.

Oil sucked out of the earth and stored in tanks is but a fraction of what is generally spoken of as "reserves." The potential capacity of a field is considered the real reserve. Such reserves are only educated guesses, subject to expansion or contraction as new exploratory wells are drilled on the outskirts of a field. These exploratory wells determine the full extent of the field, hence are of an importance out of all proportion to their particular production or cost.

The potential reserves of petroleum are far greater than the actual or known reserves, as is pointed out by President Reese Taylor who, like other Union hunters, is far from satisfied with the existing methods for secondary recovery of petroleum.

"When you realize that with the industry's present methods of recovery we get less than a third of the potential crude in a given field, you can see that the great potential source of crude exists right in our present producing properties," says Taylor. "That is why we are conducting extensive experiments with water flooding, gas drive, pressure maintenance, and reservoir heating. If secondary recovery technique can be perfected on an economic scale, it may make us revise all present estimates of recoverable crude."

# CHAPTER NINE

# Men against Millions

LYMAN STEWART'S adroit strategy for controlling the Union Oil Company fired anew the battle that grew into a quarter century war for an oil empire. Starting out as a feud between Californians, it spread to a nationwide front, then flared into an international struggle, making Union a factor in world petroleum affairs, and a far cry from the struggling little oil partnership launched by Lyman Stewart and Wallace Hardison in drowsy Pico Canyon and sleepy Santa Paula.

When in 1898 Thomas R. Bard forced the Stewarts to accede to his demands that the Hardison & Stewart Oil Company, the Sespe Oil Company, and the Torrey Canyon Oil Company be dissolved and their shares of Union Oil stock be distributed, he believed that it was just a question of time until, by buying up additional shares of the Union Oil stock as they came on the market, he could gain control of the company and bring the Stewart regime to an end. Instead, he

launched a corporate Frankenstein which was soon to destroy him as an influence in the oil business. Explaining the devious moves of this financial monster is about as simple as clarifying the Milky Way.

Stewart knew that, should Bard succeed in buying up sufficient stock to control Union, he, Stewart, was through. Bard's threat to Director R. W. Fenn of the Torrey Canyon Oil Company that he would "wreck the Union Oil Company" to gain his ends was a tip-off to Stewart. Calling a group of his friends among the stockholders to his home, Stewart laid before them his big idea. He proposed to organize in absolute secrecy a holding company that would prevent the Bard interests from gaining control of Union Oil.

Early in 1899 the conspirators organized the United Petroleum Company with a capital of $1,500,000 consisting of 15,-000 shares at $100 par each. Immediately upon incorporation, United Petroleum offered to exchange two shares of its stock for one share of stock in the Hardi-

153

*Lyman Stewart, "Father of the Western Petroleum Industry," six months before his death.*

son & Stewart Oil Company. This offer was accepted by the owners of about two-thirds of the stock of Hardison & Stewart Oil Company.

Shortly after this, the Hardison & Stewart Oil Company, owners of 36,730 shares of Union Oil Company of California stock, was disincorporated, as were the Torrey Canyon and Sespe Oil companies. The United Petroleum Company, being the owner of 7,341 shares of Hardison & Stewart stock, received in exchange 26,941.47 Union Oil shares. With only 14,682 shares of its own stock outstanding and owning 26,941 shares of Union Oil Company of California stock, each United Petroleum share was worth 1.835 shares of Union Oil. By means of this involved financial juggling, Lyman Stewart hoped to be able to thwart Bard. The objective of United Petroleum was revealed in two letters written by Stewart to the Reverend W. J. Chichester of Titusville, an old friend of Stewart and a stockholder in Hardison & Stewart.

"The new company is simply an association of the stockholders to hold control of Union for the purpose of ensuring a stable policy, and also to enable those entering it to realize a better price in case of a sale," Stewart wrote.

"With the control thus lodged in a single company where it is subject to the action of the board of directors instead of a single individual," he explained in another letter, "there can be not only a safer and more stable policy adopted for Union, but a much more advantageous price can be obtained in case of a sale by being able to sell the control of an established company."

Bard was caught napping by Stewart's tactics. Not until Stewart had virtually lined up control of Union did Bard get the slightest inkling of what was going on. When he did learn, Bard, too, swung into action. In the spring of 1899, about three months after Stewart had launched United Petroleum, Bard called together his friends and associates in the Union Oil Company. They organized the United Stockholders' Associates, to which they transferred their shares of Union Oil stock. On the assumption that Stewart didn't yet have control, they went to work to line up more stock than Stewart could control through United Petroleum. In this financial fight, the public was confused. The battle occurred in the midst of one of the wildest speculative oil-stock booms in California history. Investors figured that if both Stewart and Bard wanted Union Oil stocks, they should buy them, too. They bought not only Union but stocks in new companies, many of which had no oil wells or oil lands, even under lease.

The showdown came on November 28, 1899, at the annual stockholders' meeting of the Union Oil Company, when United Petroleum Company and United Stockholders' Associates came out in the open for the first time. Tellers began counting the stock controlled by each holding company. United Petroleum, represented by Lyman Stewart, held 26,941 shares of stock. United Stockholders' Associates, represented by Thomas R. Bard, held 16,685 shares; and there were 6,374 unpledged shares. Quickly checking over the figures, Bard realized that even if he could buy all of the 6,374 unpledged shares, he would still fall far short of

155

having enough to control the company. Lyman Stewart and associates could always outvote him.

Elected as officers of the company were Lyman Stewart, president; W. L. Stewart, vice-president and general manager; Alexander Waldie, treasurer; W. A. Carney, secretary; R. W. Clark, assistant secretary. Bard remained a director. Hundreds of new investors became Union Oil Company shareholders for the first time. There might have been more, except for the fact that wildcat oil stocks were floating around at extremely low prices.

"The state has gone oil mad," reported the *Los Angeles Express*. "A feeling of speculative unrest is abroad. Los Angeles operators just in from Kern County say that a large number of people in that county appear to be actually oil crazed. The county has been staked off by prospectors for miles in all directions from Coalinga, and men, and women too, are up there holding down claims with shotguns. Others have built barbed-wire fences around their possessions, fearful that the land or the precious stuff underground may be carried off."

Having been named United States senator, Bard wanted to get out of the oil business. The holding company he had organized, the United Stockholders' Associates, still held a big block of Union stock, roughly one-third of the shares. In Los Angeles, a group of alert young businessmen were looking for opportunities to make investments. The group consisted of J. S. Torrance, William R. Staats, Frederick H. Rindge, W. S. Botsford, and John B. Miller. Staats, who was a friend of Lyman Stewart, asked the latter where

his group might most profitably invest in an up-and-coming new oil industry. Sensing an opportunity to be of service not only to his friend but himself, Stewart suggested that Staats try to buy from Bard the holdings in United Stockholders' Associates. The Staats group secured an option, late in 1900, to buy the United Stockholders' block of stock from Bard and his friends. Staats had to raise more money. One of the bankers he approached for a loan wrote Bard asking his reasons for selling stock in a company which appeared as promising as did Union Oil. Bard's reply was revealing.

"For some time the Stewarts have been desirous of expanding the business beyond the scope of our original scheme, and for such purpose to borrow or otherwise raise large sums of money," he wrote. "This we might consent to if the management were entrusted to more competent and conservative men, but we oppose the present proposal to increase the capital from 5 million to 10 million dollars.

"The Stewarts are honest and, in the best sense, trustworthy. But they are not competent to carry on the great business of the company and are unwilling to trust it to more capable men. I learn, however, that they have indicated to our option holders that they are disposed to let the new men share in the management. They have come to the realization that the new blood is needed to give the body corporate new health and vigor."

Bard made his final exit from Union on December 18, 1900, when his resigna-

*Torrey Canyon field as it appeared in 1897 when Union Oil's entire production for the year was around 125,000 barrels, and 56,000 barrels of it came from these few wells.*

tion as director was accepted. The Torrance-Staats syndicate, purchasing the holdings of the United Stockholders' Associates, bought in as an investment and "to furnish new blood and eliminate the friction of the Bard interests," as Torrance later explained. Torrance advocated getting rid of the two holding companies, considering them a menace to Union Oil because they automatically created factions within the company. Lyman Stewart, too, agreed to dissolve United Petroleum Company if United Stockholders' Associates were disbanded. But Torrance

didn't push the idea of dissolving. Later he changed his mind and even favored continuing United Petroleum as a means of stabilizing the direction of Union Oil after United Stockholders' Associates dissolved.

"I regarded the services of Lyman Stewart as worth more to Union Oil than all the other directors put together," Torrance said. "His salary was insignificant as compared with the value of his services. He possessed courage that was almost unlimited; he knew every feature of the oil business, the drilling end, the territorial

157

end, the marketing end. But I did not have very much respect for his ability as a financier."

But the holding companies were confusing to the public, and it was difficult to make even bank presidents understand the relationship between them and the parent company. In time Lyman Stewart's control of Union Oil brought about the very one-man decisions he feared most from Bard. Only it was Lyman Stewart who made them, precipitating Union into a quarter century of turmoil.

With the Bard interests out and Lyman Stewart at the helm, enjoying the full support of the new directors, things began to hum. In January, 1900, the Board approved the formation of the Union Oil Well.Supply Company, which Bard had successfully blocked for several months. This later became the great Union Tool Company. The tanker "Santa Paula" was ordered built, with a capacity of 8,200 barrels. The first geological department in the oil industry was organized. A marketing depot was opened in Los Angeles. A pipeline from McKittrick to the sea was ordered. This was just the beginning of an expansion program which changed Union Oil from a local to an international organization.

It took a lot of money. The board increased the capital stock from 5 million to 10 million dollars, a move overwhelmingly approved by the stockholders. Lyman Stewart still had to do a lot of money raising to carry out his expansion program. He even borrowed from the Protestant Episcopal Church Diocese of Los Angeles, first $8,153 and later $16,-

000 more at 6 per cent. He and Milton Stewart loaned the company money and they even tapped Thomas Bard for a few thousand dollars. In 1901 Union moved into Hawaii. The next year they invaded South American and Alaskan markets. They built a new refinery at Bakersfield, laid out pipelines, and added storage capacity. The expansion took so much capital that they had to reduce the dividends in 1902 from $1.35 to 70 cents per quarter.

W. L. Stewart, backed by his father, proposed on August 7, 1901, that Union include some of its properties in a proposed combination of independents, but the new directors, particularly Torrance and Botsford, balked, indicating that the Stewarts could still be challenged by their own board. Nevertheless the directors went on record as favoring a consolidation of the fuel-oil interests of the state and, in addition, a system of pipelines connecting the various oil fields with tidewater. Thus was born the germ of an intriguing idea that kept bobbing up for years, namely, using Union as a nucleus around which to build an oil company big enough to challenge the mighty Standard and Royal Dutch Shell.

In October, 1902, Secretary W. A. Carney reported that "within the past year the company has expended for new ships, additions to pipelines and tankage, a new refinery plant, and additional oil territory, approximately $700,000, from which investment it has as yet received practically no revenue, inasmuch as this new plant is just coming into operation, so that the earnings of the company for

*Oleum Refinery's original four stills of 1896 were increased five-fold in the early years of the present century as the great "Offshore Selling Program" of Stewart and Baker got under way. By 1903 the plant looked like this.*

the past year or so have been chiefly received from properties previously acquired."

Then Secretary Carney warned that there was even more expense to come. Before the year was up, Union was borrowing $50,000 to $100,000 at a crack. Lyman Stewart had taken options on 60,000 acres of valuable oil lands in Santa Barbara County, an extremely fortunate acquisition because it led to the

development of the great Santa Maria field. To enable the president to cinch deals like this, the board authorized him to borrow as much as $100,000 without even consulting the directors. At the same meeting in January, they guaranteed the 3-million-dollar bond issue of the Union Transportation Company, a tanker subsidiary. Things were moving fast, even for the Stewarts.

While this expansion program was at

159

*Edward L. Doheny, petroleum pioneer, touched off scramble for oil in Los Angeles.*

its height, the Standard Oil Company made its third attempt to swallow Union Oil. Standard opened negotiations in 1903, offering to buy Union's refineries, marketing, and transportation facilities, leaving Union in the business of producing and selling crude petroleum. This was exactly what Bard and Stewart had fought about for many years. It was the setup which Bard wanted and the one which Stewart opposed. Surprisingly, at this time Stewart did not turn down the Standard offer. Instead, he made a counterproposal, offering to consider the Standard deal if Standard would agree to sign a contract to purchase 40 million barrels of crude

160

oil from Union. This seemed like an ocean of oil at the time. Standard abruptly called off negotiations and adopted new tactics that were to cause Union's directors plenty of concern.

A few weeks after the Standard deal fell through, Edward L. Doheny, the man who had touched off the great Los Angeles oil-field boom in the middle nineties, was invited to join Union's board of directors. Doheny was permitted to buy 1,000 shares of Union's treasury stock at $60, with an option on 1,500 more at the same price, although, as the executive committee had previously stated, "The company's oil properties and other resources are so valuable that the directors have hesitated to dispose of any of the treasury stock, considering it inadvisable to do so owing to its intrinsic value being much greater than the market price."

"We all wanted the benefit of Mr. Doheny's counsel," explained Lyman Stewart. "There was no personal or private reason for his election. I certainly had no power over him, and only on one occasion did I attempt to influence him." This occasion was when Doheny offered a resolution, which Stewart opposed, that Lyman Stewart's salary as president of Union Oil be increased from $3,000 a year to $1,000 a month. Stewart had worked for the modest wages of $5 a day, less than his oil drillers got, until in 1903 when he asked the board to give him an annual salary of $3,000 so that he wouldn't have to keep a daily expense account.

By the end of 1904 it looked as though the Stewarts were again in danger of losing their control of Union Oil Company.

This unit at the Los Angeles refinery converts gas oil into high-octane gasoline in the presence of a clay catalyst at the rate of 15,000 barrels of gas oil a day.

The company needed money; J. S. Torrance, manager of the finance department, reported that the bonds of the Union Transportation Company had not been sold, and Union Oil Company had to borrow money to finance Union Transportation. To free Union from its embarrassing floating indebtedness, the company needed $1,100,000. A group of Los Angeles financiers, including some of Union's directors but not the Stewarts, had offered to form a new corporation, the Union Stock and Bond Company, for the purpose of buying Union Oil securities. With each $850 bond it was proposed to sell 14 shares of stock at $60 per share, con-siderably less than the market value. Though Lyman Stewart concurred, somewhat reluctantly, with the scheme, it never got fully under way.

It didn't need to. Almost overnight, the financial picture changed. Up in the Santa Maria oil field the biggest gusher so far drilled on the North American continent came in with a roar. Hartnell No. 1 produced a million barrels of oil in the first hundred days. This was the equivalent of 1.5 million dollars. The public rushed to buy Union Oil stock.

Along with the gusher of oil came other gushers of rumors. Everybody on Spring Street, the Los Angeles financial row, was

161

whispering to everybody else that Standard Oil Company already secretly owned Union Oil Company. These rumors Lyman Stewart emphatically denied, declaring that "the policy of Union Oil Company of California in the future will be, as it has been in the past, that of an independent producer without alliances." But the rumors continued, and from time to time Stewart had to repeat his denial, declaring that "neither is your company nor any of its auxiliaries interested, directly or indirectly, in the Standard or any of its auxiliaries or allied companies."

New issues of Union Oil stock in 1905 were snapped up in such quantities by the investing public that it was doubtful if the Stewarts could maintain control of the company, even with the block of United Petroleum Company shares they had under their thumb. Appreciating that one holding company had saved them in 1899, Lyman Stewart decided that another might save him in 1905. He and his family and close associates organized, in June of that year, the Union Provident Company, capitalized at 5 million dollars, with United Petroleum holding a controlling interest in the new corporation. The new company's articles of incorporation declared that it was formed "to buy shares of the Union Oil Company to the extent of not more than 50,000 shares," a limitation increased later to 250,000 shares when Union Provident's capitalization was boosted to 25 million dollars.

The operation of Union Provident Company was nothing short of financial wizardry. From time to time, as stock was offered for sale by Union Oil, the stockholders of United Petroleum and Union Provident were allowed to participate in the offering on the condition that one-half of their subscription would be for stock of Union Oil and one-half for stock of Union Provident. By this means the smaller United Petroleum was able to control the larger Union Provident Company, which in turn controlled the giant Union Oil Company and its subsidiaries, which by this time added up to 20. Sometime later W. L. Stewart was asked why the Stewarts didn't simply acquire enough stock in the already well-established United Petroleum Company to control Union Oil Company.

"It could have been done at that particular time," he replied, "but there were in mind plans for great expansion and development of Union Oil which could not have been handled that way. We did not have the money. There was a gap between the majority of the outstanding shares of Union Oil Company and the number of shares held by the United Petroleum Company. This we had to close."

By means of their ingenious holding-company's holding of a holding company which held the main company, which controlled 20 subsidiaries, the Stewarts, with roughly a one-eighth interest, were able to keep an ironclad control over Union Oil

*Amid orange and lemon groves along the Santa Clara river near Santa Paula are both old and new wells of Union Oil which had its beginning in this neighborhood.*

Company—until a day of reckoning came a decade later. At the time holding companies were considered legal, and Lyman Stewart's device for controlling Union Oil was considered legitimate.

Will Stewart knew whereof he spoke when he talked of plans for great expansion and development and more issues. Before 1905 had closed, Union had formed, in cooperation with the Michigan Steamship Company, a new subsidiary known as Union Steamship Company. It was capitalized at 5 million dollars, and the funds were to buy four more tankers. Frank Garbutt, head of the department, wanted at least half a million dollars within the next six months. John Baker, Jr., of the sales department wanted half a million every six months for his plans of expansion, including five large steamers to cost a million dollars each. J. S. Torrance of the finance department pointed out that the company needed $2,700,000 to meet expenses for conversion of ships, purchase of 2,365 acres of Rancho El Cajon de Santa Ana land, payments on ships, on tankers, and on the extended pipeline system.

To raise the money, 8,000 shares of Union Oil treasury stock were sold at $164 a share. By the end of 1907, a total of 78,000 shares had been issued. Lyman Stewart was feeling more aggressive and expansive than ever before. Union's capital was increased from 10 million to 50 million dollars. He had surrounded himself with men who were expansive, men r'aring to drive ahead. John Baker of the San Francisco office said he could line up lucrative contracts in South America, but wanted to be sure of an adequate supply

before signing them. Lyman Stewart replied at a directors' meeting, "If there is any question, even the slightest, about the quantity of oil to meet these contracts, we will put more tools in the field; if necessary, we will run thirty, forty, fifty strings of tools in our territory. You get the contracts, we'll get the oil."

With such spirit pervading the management, Baker wrote to Stewart on January 17, 1907, saying, "Our company in the short space of twelve months has risen from local to national prominence, and at the time occupies a very prominent position in the oil business of the world. Our transportation facilities, together with our Panama pipeline, enable us to reach the markets of the world."

Expanding at this rate meant more money, more millions. The millions were raised by selling more stock. Union stock was selling in the open market at $105 a share. The company offered rights to stockholders at $95 a share, with a special plan whereby employees could buy at the same price. Stockholders and employees took 3 million dollars' worth. This stock bought by employees was to play a decisive role in later years when the battles for control again became decisive. At the time Union Provident managed to pick up enough shares so that through United Petroleum the Stewarts could maintain their control.

On June 21, 1908, there occurred a significant incident which attracted no particular attention at the time. To meet immediate financial requirements, Lyman Stewart underwrote $375,000 worth of stock being sold on the market. Fortunately the issue was oversubscribed, and

Lyman Stewart didn't have to take any stock. However, under the terms of his subscription he was entitled to an underwriter's commission of 2½ per cent. This he refused, asking the treasurer to turn the money over to "a fund for the purpose of promoting temperance and morality among the men through the advancement of their general welfare."

Lyman Stewart was becoming a reformer. He crusaded for the gospel as ardently as he had striven for oil. It was the beginning of a warp in his judgment that caused the company no end of embarrassment and, indeed, almost wrecked it. Late in 1909 he appointed Robert Watchorn, a former commissioner of immigration, to the strategic position of treasurer of Union Oil. Asked why he had chosen Watchorn, who had no previous experience, either as a financier or as an oil man, Stewart naïvely said, "Mr. Watchorn is a very popular man. Every time he appears at a Presbyterian Convention he is greeted with a Chautauqua salute." Though other members of the board acquiesced to the appointment, they did not share Stewart's confidence in Watchorn's ability. Some of them flatly declared that he was incompetent.

With Watchorn's appointment was launched a period of high finance, in which he and Stewart reached for millions, not only to finance Union Oil expansion but also to found the Bible Institute of Los Angeles, to support missionaries in China, and to "provide a Bible for every Chinaman." Stewart needed money not only to develop and handle more oil but also to underwrite his enormous benefactions.

By 1910 he had persuaded the stockholders to approve a bonded indebtedness of 20 million dollars for Union Oil Company. Watchorn went to New York to get money, since Union's demands had outgrown the California money marts. Lyman Stewart was seriously ill, and unfortunately this permitted Watchorn to have far more leeway in Union's financial affairs than Stewart originally intended. Watchorn negotiated a deal with Hallgarten and Company of New York to underwrite a bond issue of 5 million dollars. The Hallgarten firm extracted its pound of flesh in the form of a "negative option" that prohibited Union from selling more than 1.5 million dollars' worth of new stock during the next thirty years without Hallgarten's consent, an option that was fortunately terminated when the Hallgarten company ran out of ready money.

Union's financial position became so precarious in 1913 that George H. Burr and Company, which had handled around a million-and-a-half's worth of Union's paper, threatened to throw the company into a receivership if obligations were not paid immediately. A note amounting to a million dollars was falling due in May, and another for a similar amount was due in August. Another $700,000 was needed for obligations to develop the Outer Harbor Dock and Wharf Company, another Union subsidiary. Watchorn was unable to raise the money in New York. W. L. Stewart succeeded in getting a million dollars from a Los Angeles group.

While Union was in this precarious financial position, Watchorn persuaded Lyman Stewart to sign a paper giving Watchorn an option on all of the Stewart

165

holdings in not only the United Petroleum Company and the Union Provident Company but likewise all of Stewart's Union Oil shares. At the time Lyman Stewart was a sick man, confined to his bed. His wife had passed away only a few months before. Lyman Stewart thought his end was near. Both he and his brother Milton wanted more money for their religious benefactions. The option, which entitled the holder to buy all the Stewart holdings at $150 per share, was one way to get money quickly. Watchorn sold his option for 1 million dollars to Eugene de Sabla, president of Esperanza Consolidated, which shortly after became the General Petroleum Company.

The option soon became "the million-dollar mystery," an important and still elusive episode in Union Oil history. De Sabla made the first payment of $500,000, agreeing to pay the rest at the rate of $33,000 a month. After the initial payment, Watchorn gave Lyman Stewart a check for $493,177, which money Stewart used to meet personal obligations and to distribute among members of the Stewart family. In return for the check, Stewart gave Watchorn securities to the value of the check, which were turned over by Watchorn to the trustees of the Bible Institute; subsequently monthly payments by

de Sabla were also delivered to the Bible Institute. Later a violent argument broke out between Watchorn and Lyman Stewart as to the use of these monies for benevolent purposes.

Lyman Stewart contended, when he recovered, that he had given Watchorn an option only on his interests in Union Provident and United Petroleum companies. He had signed the option in blank, and Watchorn had included in it the stock that Stewart held directly in the Union Oil Company. The option itself became a tremendous threat over the Union Oil Company, particularly when Eugene de Sabla delivered it to the rival General Petroleum Company. General Petroleum, unable to exercise the option, assigned it to the Mercantile Trust Company of San Francisco. Later the trust company assigned it to Andrew Weir and H. Tilden Smith, British financiers and oil men. Although it was never exercised, the option, until it expired in April, 1914, remained a dark cloud over Union's financial picture.

The million-dollar mystery was only one of several threats hanging over Union Oil's financial security. An even more crucial threat was made by a new character on the scene named John H. Garrigues, who represented George H. Burr and Company, the New York house that

166

*Four companies use this absorption plant to eliminate duplication and insure the most efficient conservation of field's resources.*

had loaned Union Oil Company $1,600,-000. When payment became due early in 1913, Union didn't have the money. Garrigues, as the Pacific Coast agent for Burr, declared, "If the notes are not paid at maturity, I'll throw you into the hands of a receiver." As an alternative, he had a proposition: The first condition was that he be elected treasurer of the Union Oil Company at a salary of $25,000 a year; the second was that he be given a free hand in Union's financing. Garrigues agreed to get Union $1,100,000 from Burr and Company immediately. Back to the wall, Lyman Stewart persuaded the Union directors to employ Garrigues as treasurer "as insurance—as cheap insurance as we could get."

Garrigues was a forceful character with unshakable confidence in himself and able to turn on gushers of ego at the slightest provocation. Immediately upon becoming treasurer he began to wield a heavy hand in an autocratic and highly dictatorial manner. First of all he demanded and obtained the resignations of the former treasurer, the auditor, the comptroller, the manager of the marine department, the manager of the manufacturing department, and numerous lesser figures from Union Oil. He insisted that A. P. Johnson be elected to the board to represent "minority stockholders." Most important, pointing out that his agreement with Union gave him a "free hand in financing," he ordered dividends suspended and forced Lyman Stewart on December 18, 1914, to write to stockholders saying:

"Suspension or reduction of dividends is not due to losses or any falling off in earnings. The situation has been brought about chiefly by too much prosperity. The volume of the company's business has doubled in the past four years with no corresponding increase in capital stock. Growing by leaps and bounds year after year from 10 million dollars gross sales on a capital of 30 million dollars to 20 million dollars on a capital of 32 million dollars, this great flow of new business has required each year millions of dollars for fixed investment in oil lands, drilling operations, pipelines, storage equipment, ships, manufacturing facilities, and new stations.

"At this date the entire outstanding indebtedness and serial note obligations in the hands of the public, including both the

168

direct bonded debt of the Union Oil Company of California, its wholly owned and its controlled companies guaranteed by it, totals $12,653,000."

Refinancing to meet payments due on this enormous debt kept the Union directors continually uneasy. Early in 1914 Hallgarten and Company of New York reported that it would be unable to carry out the terms of its agreement. At the time Union needed a million dollars which Hallgarten was to provide, and needed it urgently and immediately. A syndicate of Los Angeles financiers offered to put up the million dollars on debenture gold notes, but they made a drastic and shocking condition to this offer. Lyman Stewart must resign as president of the Union Oil Company before any more money would

be forthcoming. Originally the syndicate also insisted on having six of the eleven directors on the board, but this was not carried out.

"We felt that, on account of the Watchorn option which Lyman Stewart had given, the investing public had to a certain extent lost confidence in the Union Oil Company," explained John E. Jardine, head of the syndicate.

With Union desperate for ready money, Lyman Stewart presented his resignation on April 22, 1914. The directors immediately elected William L. Stewart, his son, as president to succeed him. Lyman Stewart was pushed upstairs to be chairman of the board. Thus for want of a million dollars, Lyman Stewart lost control of a 30-million-dollar oil empire.

But he was by no means through. The

*Underground pressure in the Cat Canyon field of Santa Barbara county is assured by this gas injection plant. Gas from which natural gasoline has been extracted is pushed back into the oil formations to aid in further recovery of the field's petroleum reserve.*

*Modern oil production requires comparatively little space as this Union Oil well in the Orcutt Field shows. While it keeps on pumping, the surrounding land produces crops.*

day before he stepped out of office, Lyman Stewart had signed a contract, with the approval of the board, with two new figures on the Union Oil horizon. They were Andrew Weir and H. Tilden Smith, representing British interests. Weir and Smith had picked up the expired de Sabla option, originally given by Lyman Stewart to Robert Watchorn. The Britishers proposed to organize a new company, known as the British Union Oil Company, which would purchase 150,000 shares of Union Oil treasury stock at par, a deal involving 15 million dollars. Heading the British syndicate, but discreetly in the background, was Earl Grey, former Governor General of Canada. The 15 million dollars offered by the Britishers would more than wipe out Union's embarrassing debts. The British in turn would receive Union's oil production to fuel the British fleet. In secret British fleet maneuvers, a few bat-

tleships converted to oil had not only outmaneuvered but outsped and outlasted the attacking coal-burner fleets so spectacularly that the Admiralty decided to replace coal with oil on all British ships. The Admiralty was anticipating war with Germany, and this was a major consideration with the British in making a heavy investment in oil.

Soon after the contract was signed, the British made the first payment of $2,500,-000. The second payment, due in August, 1914, was never paid because by that time war had broken out and the British had no time to convert their ships. The Union directors extended the date for completing the $15,000,000 transaction for one year. The British, caught in a life-and-death struggle with the Kaiser, were never able to complete it. This time, instead of forfeiting the down payment of $2,500,000, as Eugene de Sabla had done on his

*Union's South Mountain Field near Santa Paula is in midst of verdant beauty.*

*Skimming pond in Brea Canyon. Here water is allowed to settle out of the oil as it comes from wells. The clean oil is then skimmed off the top and sent to refineries.*

million-dollar option, Weir and Smith received stock to the value of $2,500,000. The British deal was finally called off on March 22, 1915, but the block of stock in British hands made Union, for the first time, an international company. It also became another big question mark over the company's future.

Hardly had the British deal fizzled out than Edward L. Doheny, former director of Union Oil, made a bid to secure control of the company. Doheny and associates were forming the Pan American Oil and Transportation Company, which they hoped to make big enough to compete on even terms with Standard Oil and the Royal Dutch Shell. Doheny offered to buy 51 per cent of the stock of Union Oil at $85 per share, and also proposed to buy up several other Western oil companies. The offer was turned down by the Union directors.

But the dream of another company big enough to compete with the giants on a world-wide scale continued. One reason the directors were so ready to turn down Doheny was that key oil men representing more than 150 independent companies in California were already busy on plans to form a 100 million dollar corporation to compete with Standard and Dutch Shell for the oil markets of the world.

This merger of the little fellows to make another giant got off to a flying start in the summer of 1915 when a conference was attended by W. L. Stewart, representing the Union Oil Company; T. A. O'Donnell, representing the California Petroleum Corporation; L. P. St. Clair and Mark Requa, representing the Independent Oil Producers Agency; J. T. Currie, representing Andrew Weir and British interests. Requa was the key man in this ambitious scheme. The idea was to build the new oil colossus around Union, which was already a small giant on its own. To do this, Requa needed an appraisal of the properties of 150 oil companies, including Union, because the basis on which the companies were to be admitted to the great merger was that of physical valuation and properties. Capitalization was to have nothing to do with the case. However, Requa did need an option on the Union Oil stock controlled by the Stewarts in order to line up the financing in New York, where Bernard M. Baruch, Solomon and Company, Hayden Stone and Company, and other tycoons of finance had indicated a willingness to put up the money.

The other independents looked to Union to take the lead in the merger. Union's board showed no initiative in working out the deal, which was bitterly opposed by Treasurer John Garrigues. In meetings, Garrigues went out of his way to be arrogant and ruthless with the independent producers, all of whom had been very friendly with Union Oil. Many had been associated with Union for years, since Union acted as their sales agent. The independents had their own associa-tion headed by T. A. O'Donnell, who reported after one meeting that Garrigues had made demands of the group and wound up by pounding the table, declaring:

"Refuse and I will not spend another dollar on transportation facilities. I will put 100 strings of tools to work and get my own production. In the meantime I will take advantage of every technicality in the written agency agreement to transport and sell your oil and force every member of the agency into bankruptcy."

"You talk as if you were the whole Union Oil Company," replied O'Donnell.

"I am the whole Union Oil Company," shouted Garrigues.

After this flare-up, a peace meeting was called. Garrigues met with the executive committee of the Independent Oil Producers Agency. S. A. Guiberson, Jr., of San Francisco, a well-known independent oil operator, reported what happened.

"Garrigues said that he was the Moses who had come out to California to lead us out of our troubles," said Guiberson. "Then he said that he had been sent to California to do four things. First, to acquire control of the lumber industry of the Pacific Coast; second, to acquire control of the oil industry of the Pacific Coast; third, to dominate and control the financial interests of the Pacific Coast; fourth, to change and direct the politics of the Pacific Coast. 'Nothing can prevent me from accomplishing my purpose, not even the Standard Oil, and you can get on my band wagon and ride through to the goal or you can get in the road and get run over.' "

Requa ran into other difficulties in

173

*In sharp contrast to many oil pipeline pumping stations, Union Oil's Santa Margarita plant is on cool, wooded slopes of the coastal range. Three lines pass through here, carrying oil from San Joaquin valley to Avila where it is loaded into tank ships.*

getting his Union Oil stock option. Milton Stewart had signed power of attorney to Reverend W. E. Blackstone, a former missionary to China who was manager of the Stewart philanthropic enterprises. Garrigues, opposing the option, told Reverend Blackstone that he, Garrigues, was guided by occult sources. The Reverend Blackstone, in turn, said that he prayed for divine guidance. The missionary's prayers were evidently stronger than Garrigues's occult guidance, because Requa eventually got the option from the entire Stewart family to purchase their 57,000 shares at around $95 a share.

Requa was never able to complete the deal, because the Stewart option was subject to getting a similar option on the big block of stock held by Andrew Weir and Tilden Smith. The Britishers had other designs, but before these came out into the open Union went through another internal spasm provoked by the exuberant Garrigues.

On July 15, 1915, Garrigues persuaded Director Giles Kellogg to offer a resolution increasing the treasurer's salary to $50,000 a year. This was bitterly opposed by President W. L. Stewart and William R. Staats, another director. Garrigues offered to resign then and there. Although the majority of the directors wanted to get rid of him, they hesitated to accept his resignation, fearing the financial strength they believed he held. A final blowup came on January 13, 1916, when Garrigues again attempted to dictate to the board. This time they removed him from office and replaced him with William L. Stewart, who became both president and treasurer. Thus was precipitated the bitterest legal battle in Union's tempestuous history.

Immediately after being ousted, Gar-rigues formed the Union Oil Company Stockholders Protective Association. In the name of the association, he filed a suit to dissolve the two holding companies by which the Stewarts controlled the Union Oil Company. Public meetings were held, the fight was taken to the newspapers. The Stewarts were not backward about getting into the fight. Bitter charges and countercharges were hurled in the vicious battle even before it could come into the court of Judge Louis M. Myers. During the long trial, in the course of which all of Union's dirty linen was washed in public, the Stewart family voluntarily dissolved the Union Provident Company. Thus when Judge Myers decided against the Stewarts in a sweeping decision on October 2, 1916, there was only one holding company, United Petro-

*Through this dehydrator unit in the Brea Canyon field wet oil (containing water) is passed until it meets pipeline requirements—not more than 3 per cent water content.*

leum, to unscramble. The court decided that the system of holding-company control by which Lyman Stewart and his family, owning one-eighth of the stock of a 50-million-dollar corporation, could dominate its affairs for years, was illegal and must end.

"I never sought to control Union Oil Company for any personal reason," Lyman Stewart explained. "I never desired to be kept in office, except upon merit. The one idea in having control of the company was to ensure its stability of management. The Stewarts hold 57,000 shares of stock in the company. They have a selfish interest in making them valuable. In making them valuable, they have made the shares of every other stockholder valuable."

The court's decision against the Stewarts provoked a furious proxy battle in 1916, during which the Garrigues faction and the Stewart forces appealed for support in the forthcoming annual meeting. When the meeting, twice postponed, was called on February 22, 1917, at Oleum (to which the head office had been moved in the course of a feud with Los Angeles City officials over taxes), the Stewarts enjoyed more support, through popular choice, than they had previously through the system of holding companies. They won all but two of the eleven seats on the board of directors; Garrigues and one associate who won the other two soon ceased to be important factors in the company affairs.

Union was no longer a family company. The Stewarts themselves no longer voted as a block. Father and son did not see eye to eye. Chairman Lyman Stewart and

President William Stewart often were on opposite sides of questions before the board.

By this time Lyman Stewart had bounced back from death's door to good health. On August 26, 1916, he married his secretary, Lulu M. Crowell, with whom he had kindred evangelical interests, particularly in the Bible Institute.

Lyman Stewart frequently said that son Will Stewart was too conservative. Will Stewart frequently replied that he wouldn't be so conservative if his father didn't want to buy all the oil land in California. This difference in viewpoint between father and son was graphically illustrated when they clashed head-on over a proposal to buy the Pinal-Dome Oil Company for $3,600,000. Lyman Stewart proposed it and argued in the affirmative. Will Stewart, with the support of John Garrigues, objected strenuously. Father defeated son in this affair, for the board voted for the purchase, but often the outcome was the other way around.

Union was still growing like Topsy. Oil wells, pipelines, tankers, service stations cost additional thousands. On April 6, 1919, the board approved increasing the capitalization from 50 million to 100 million dollars. This move caught the attention of important Eastern oil and financial interests. In July Henry Lockhart, Jr., wrote to the directors that he was authorized on behalf of a group of bankers operating as a syndicate to offer to buy 20 million dollars' worth of Union Oil's stock. Needing the money badly, the directors accepted. It turned out that the syndicate, known as the Commonwealth Petroleum Company, was a partnership composed of Percy Rockefeller, Henry Lockhart, Jr., and Charles H. Sabin, head of the Guaranty Trust Company of New York. Thus Wall Street made its bid for control of the giant young oil company developed by Westerners.

The new purchasers denied any intentions of wanting to control Union Oil, but the public, always suspicious of Wall Street, doubted them. Los Angeles newspapers and financiers and even President W. L. Stewart issued statements declaring that the newcomers had no intention of controlling Union, claiming that the company was owned by upwards of four thousand stockholders, most of them Californians but many scattered over the balance of the United States and Great Britain.

Then, without warning, came word that the syndicate had bought the block of stock held by Andrew Weir and the other Britishers who had come in at the opening of World War I. This put an entirely different light on the Wall Street deal, as did the organization of a new corporation known as Union Oil of Delaware, announced in September, 1919. Union of Delaware began picking up other blocks of Union of California stock, and likewise the stock of the Columbia Oil Producing Company of California, organized by Wallace Hardison. A scramble for Union stock sent it up to over $200 a share. Finally in December, 1920, the Union directors authorized President Stewart and three other members of the board to go to New York and find out what it was all about. By this time Union of Delaware owned 126,000 shares, or approximately one-fourth of the outstanding Union of California stock. Stewart and his col-

leagues were able to persuade Percy Rockefeller that to buy another 125,000 shares on the market would cost more than the company was worth. The syndicate assured them that Union of Delaware would abandon the attempt to wrest control of Union Oil from the Californians.

The assurance was short-lived. The following May a news bomb exploded in the form of a statement that the British-controlled Royal Dutch Shell interests had bought control of Union of Delaware, giving them a one-fourth interest in Union of California. Shell brokers were reported to be busily buying up stock in the market, and on November 2, 1921, the Union Oil Company of Delaware officially announced ratification of a plan for merger of their properties with the Royal Dutch Shell Petroleum Company, which had been incorporated at The Hague in Holland in 1890, mostly with English capital.

The merger announcement set off international fireworks. In the United States Senate a resolution was introduced calling for a Federal investigation of this attempt of foreign interests to take over a big American oil company. Stockholders large and small rallied to prevent the Britishers from grabbing Union Oil. In a short time it became a "no-holds-barred" fight for control of Union, this time with the foreigners against the Americans, which led to a spectacular demonstration of patriotism.

Leading the American forces was Isaac Milbank, a retired president of the Borden Milk Company, who had become a director of Union Oil of California. Milbank allied himself with the Stewarts and the other California directors in a plan to save

Union from foreign domination. It called for the pooling of sufficient stock, under the name of a new organization known as Union Oil Associates, to prevent the British grab. California investors held some 314,000 shares of Union stock. The big drive was to get these shares into the Union Oil Associates fold before the British could increase their block of 131,000 shares to more than the Californians held. The fight for the company gained momentum; newspapers editorialized; stockholders wrote letters; cartoons were published.

Then, as the battle became a public affair, Hiram E. Johnson, Jr., of San Francisco, representing a group of speculators, organized an independent pool of Union stock. This group got together all shares available for the purpose of cashing in by offering its block of stock to either the British or the Milbank-Stewart group, depending on who would pay the most. Johnson and his group soon had more than ten thousand shares, which promised to be the controlling factor. Mark Requa, who had been fuel administrator for the United States during World War I, joined the battle on the side of the Associates.

As the showdown neared in July, 1921, a survey indicated that the Milbank-Stewart group had about 35 per cent of the outstanding shares under their control, while the British had approximately 30 per cent. The Johnson pool had grabbed around 10 per cent from a floating supply. The rest was still widely held. The campaign intensified as the deadline, set for March 20, 1922, approached. If one share more than half of Union's stock could be pledged to the Associates before that midnight, the company would be saved for the Americans. Otherwise, it might pass into foreign hands. Newspapers, civic groups, rank-and-file citizens thoughtfully appealed to hesitant stockholders to support Union Oil Associates.

Calling all Americans to "do your duty," the *Los Angeles Express* pleaded:

"Roughly at midnight March 20 the wires will flash to the four corners of the world the success or failure of Californians to keep control of one of their largest and most successful institutions. On that night will be decided whether or not large areas of California's richest oil lands are to become the cat's paw for foreign exploitation, or whether they are to proceed in their orderly development for the benefit of all California.

"The manner and the very daring of the plan conceived by foreign interests to acquire control of Union Oil of California have never been equaled in the annals of the financial world for its plain audacity. That these foreign magnates could believe that Californians would walk with eyes open into their trap is anything but complimentary to Californians. Every stockholder owes it to his pocketbook, to Cali-

*Plenty of oil is being pumped here in the Orcutt Field but the derricks were removed soon after the wells came into production. Two pumping units shown here.*

178

fornia, and to his nation to keep the American flag flying over California's oil fields."

The frenzy of excitement ended on the crucial midnight of March 20, 1922. The tally showed that Union Oil Associates controlled 275,000 shares, or 24,000 more than were needed. The Johnson group in San Francisco, waiting too long, was holding the sack with a big block of shares not needed in the battle for control of Union Oil. The fight was a great personal triumph for Isaac Milbank and for Lyman Stewart, too. Both of them had come out of retirement to work day and night rounding up more stock for Union Oil Associates. The Associates, victory having been won, lost no time in incorporating a 30-million-dollar holding company which for the next ten years held 57½ per cent of the Union Oil stock. The holding company was deemed necessary, in spite of Judge Myers's previous ruling disbanding the Stewart family holding company. On December 20, 1932, the Associates were merged with the Union Oil Company when the authorized capitalization was increased to 187 million dollars. Since then no group, either family or competing company, Wall Street or foreign interest, has managed to maneuver control of Union Oil, owned by 35,000 scattered stockholders.

But the triumph was not without casualties. During the fight Isaac Milbank and Lyman Stewart met with stockholders day and night, appealed by phone and by letter, sought to contact every individual shareholder who could be reached. They fought and explained and pleaded; they did everything possible to keep the control of Union in the United States. Though they appeared tireless, the fight took its toll. When the stimulus of battle passed, both were desperately ill men. Isaac Milbank's last ounce of strength ran out on August 13, 1922, when he died just five months after he had led his forces to victory. Lyman Stewart, who had fought the gallant fight, died on the morning of September 28, 1923, at the age of eighty-three years. Milton Stewart, ill for months, followed him seven weeks later, never knowing that his beloved younger brother had gone before him.

# CHAPTER TEN

# Into the Second Half Century

As he rounded out his fifteenth year as Union's president, William L. Stewart reported to the 9,262 stockholders in February, 1930, "The Company's affairs are in a strong financial position and sound." Eight years free from factional strife had enabled the company to expand and grow into an oil empire far beyond the most optimistic dreams of the founders.

It appeared that nothing could stop the husky young business giant, as sales leaped to an all-time high of 89 million dollars in 1929, the most prosperous year in the company's history up to that time. Earnings jumped from $2.93 a share in 1928 to $3.56 in 1929. Union's assets climbed steadily from 67 million in 1914 to 370 million dollars in 1929. Capitalization had zoomed in forty years to 125 million dollars, twenty-five times the corporate worth of the company when it was launched. Union held more than 300,000 acres of oil reserves, including some of the richest fields in the country. The company's tank-ship fleet had a carrying capacity of 857 thousand barrels. It owned 725 tank cars, 1,200 miles of pipelines, had 500 bulk-distributing depots scattered over the globe, and 600 retail service stations on the Pacific Coast.

This was the bright outlook on paper. Nobody was much concerned by certain dark clouds on the horizon, harbingers of the depression thirties that would test the mettle of the Union Oil Company more ruthlessly than any period in its history, with the possible exception of the first trying decade when Lyman Stewart and Wallace Hardison kept it alive by sheer stubbornness and fortitude. Union was swept into the economic holocaust of the thirties without a Stewart hand at the helm. On June 21, 1930, four months after his cheerful report to stockholders, President William L. Stewart died suddenly of heart attack at his summer home at Hermosa Beach.

Union was no longer a family affair. The Stewarts no longer controlled the company. W. L. Stewart during his fifteen years as president had welded the various factions in the company together by his genial personality plus adroit leadership. "W. L." accomplished by persuasion what Lyman Stewart had achieved by corporate power. Of his contribution to Union's amazing growth, *The California Oil World* reported:

"To W. L. Stewart may be attributed the beginning of a systematic industrial relations activity. He had an intense interest in the problems of the employees. Men instinctively liked him, and he showed the same capacity as his father to enlist in the company's service capable, experienced workmen in all phases of the industry. He was quick to approve worthwhile effort, and believed in giving his lieutenants scope to apply their talents. About his own duties he went quietly and unobtrusively, preferring always to encourage and direct rather than drive. He was amenable to suggestions at all times. Democratic, soft-spoken, and kindly, he was nevertheless a man of decision, and Union Oil enjoyed a remarkable period of progress and prosperity under his leadership."

W. L. Stewart's death at this particular time was a major loss to the company. The Stewart family had been the amalgam that held the Union Oil Company and its many offshoot subsidiaries together. There were two Stewart sons in the company, but Will Stewart had insisted that they start at the bottom and earn their promotion by their own efforts. Son Bill— W. L., Jr.—after training as a chemical and mechanical engineer at Stanford and M.I.T. started as a laborer and handyman in the oil fields, became a pipefitter at the

Wilmington refinery, then climbed the rungs of the manufacturing department. Son Arthur Chichester Stewart—known better as Art or "A. C."—after training at Stanford University as an engineer and at Harvard School of Business Administration went to work as a wiper in tank-ship engine rooms, then found his flair for sales as a service-station attendant on the fishing docks at San Pedro. Art Stewart worked up through the sales department, learning the selling game in the field in California, Canada, China, and Japan. At the time of Will Stewart's death, Bill was thirty-three and Arthur twenty-five. In the emergency created by Will Stewart's sudden death, the directors moved swiftly, making three appointments on July 7, 1930. E. W. Clark, who had retired as executive vice-president the year before, but who had remained on the board and on the executive committee, was named chairman of the board. L. P. St. Clair, who had succeeded Clark as executive vice-president, was elected president of the company. W. L. Stewart, Jr., who had been a director since 1926, and a member of the executive committee as well as director of manufacturing since June, 1929, was made a vice-president. The new heads of Union were veterans in the California oil industry.

Clark, a native of New Hampshire, had come to California in 1897 to manage the Pacific Coast Railway Company, a narrow-gauge that ran north and south out of San Luis Obispo, serving Union's oil fields in the Santa Maria area. A founder of the Pinal-Dome Oil Company, later purchased by Union, Clark became general superintendent of the Producers'

Transportation Company in 1910 when Union and the San Joaquin Valley independents built their vital pipeline to the sea. After serving as general manager of all Union's subsidiary transportation facilities and vice-president, Clark became Union's general manager, a title that was changed to executive vice-president in 1921.

Known to everybody as "E. W.," Clark was a versatile character. He frequently turned up in the fields and at out-of-the-way pumping stations seldom visited by "the big brass," to talk with men on duty at Union's lonely stations. A founder of the American Petroleum Institute in 1919, he served two years as its president in 1927 and 1928. His hobby was fast sports-model automobiles, which he drove like Barney Oldfield. A beloved character with friends in all levels of the oil industry, Clark shunned publicity spotlights so avidly that his role in Union's growth and that of the oil industry as well is seldom appreciated. Clark served as chairman of the board until his death, May 12, 1931.

The new president chosen to pilot Union Oil through the rugged years ahead was a veteran of many an oil-field battle as the champion of the independents. L. P. "Press" St. Clair had been a moving spirit in organizing the Independent Oil Producers Agency. As its president, he jockeyed Standard and Associated into boosting the purchase price of crude paid the independent producers of the San Joaquin Valley fields from 11½ cents to 63 cents a barrel. When Standard and Associated refused to pay more, he leagued up with Will Stewart to make Union Oil

E. W. Clark, one of the most beloved men in oil industry, served Union for three decades.

the sole marketing outlet for the independents, thus doubling the flood of oil the company had to sell and pushing Union to even more activity in the world oil market. Thus "Press" St. Clair was a major factor in Union's phenomenal growth, as reported by W. L. Stewart in his 1930 report. St. Clair was the man who produced the oil that Will Stewart and John Baker, Jr., sold. For eight years previous to his selection as president, St. Clair had served as Union's vice-president.

The new president had thrived on petroleum crisis after crisis since the turn of the century. Born in Dutch Flat in the Mother Lode, he was reared in Bakersfield, where as a youngster he helped

*L. P. St. Clair, fifth president of Union Oil,*
*served from July, 1930, to October, 1938.*

his father lay the town's first gas mains. After an apprenticeship in San Francisco, St. Clair returned to manage the Bakersfield Gas & Electric Company. When the hectic Kern River oil strikes were made, he turned to oil, became a producer, championed conservation vigorously, fought the battles of the independents. With his background, "Press" St. Clair loomed as the man of the hour to pilot Union through rough years.

It was no enviable task the new president assumed. California's oil wells were pouring out an unprecedented flood of crude, 878,000 barrels a day. The market could absorb only 675,000 barrels even by dumping oil at offshore and intercoastal points at ruinous prices. Never before had there been so much oil in storage. Every tank, barrel, sump hole, or anything else capable of holding oil was running over, with nothing but mounting production in sight. Product prices were generally far below production costs. Facilities for handling crude were taxed to capacity. Crews were drilling still more wells, and they were hitting more prolific oil sands than had been yet tapped.

Adding to the dilemma, hard times were pinching the automobile industry. Factory output of automobiles skidded from 5,350,000 vehicles in 1929 to 2,500,000 in 1934. Thousands of companies had collapsed, hundreds of banks were closed. Price wars broke out in the petroleum industry as hard-pressed producers scrambled to get rid of their surplus oil. Union's sales toppled from the 89-million-dollar high to 61 million dollars during the first year of St. Clair's presidency, and fell off another 10 million dollars during the next two years. When it appeared that nothing else could stop the tide, the Pacific Coast Petroleum Agency was organized to try to stabilize production and sales. Order returned to the industry as the national economy improved. Sales began to pick up. By 1938, when St. Clair resigned, Union's sales volume was back to 83 million dollars.

The company went through the depression without passing a dividend. But it achieved this financial feat by drawing on its surplus to pay out 68 per cent more than it earned. Drastic economies were inflicted, capital expenditures were slashed. Five hundred wells were shut down, and only the bare essential of maintenance of plant and equipment was authorized. The only major new construction during the low was the $1,260,000 plant at Oleum to turn out the new Triton motor oil, which aided immensely in rebuilding sales. The

only department that was pampered at all was sales; Union needed dollars desperately—to get them, it had to market products.

A practical oil producer, St. Clair kept Union's oil hunters probing for oil. Though the number of drilling crews dropped from 46 in 1929 to 6 in 1931, Union had 20 rigs operating in 1936, and completed 83 new wells that year, some of them among Union's best producers. Many wells were shut in completely, or beaned back to a small flow. They paid off handsomely in full production later. In 1937, Union drillers finished at Santa Fe Springs the deepest well in the world at that time, 11,302 feet. In 1930 St. Clair paid $4,000,000 for an undivided one-half interest in the 160-acre King Lease in Kettleman Hills, acquired from the Amerada Petroleum Corporation. Even at the low tide of 1932, he dug deep for $2,250,000 for the purchase of an undivided one-half interest in the Getty "Armstrong" leases, comprising 1,260 acres on the North Dome of Kettleman Hills. Union was carrying out a tradition, to get the oil, even when it was swamped with crude.

The hard times had strained the company in ways even more vital than the scarcity of dollars. As Union rode out the storm, largely by living off its fat, factions developed within the management and the directorate. All of the directors and many of the stockholders realized that drastic steps had to be taken to rebuild Union's manufacturing plant and to regain the company's aggressive competitive position. But no one in the management was able to spark the entire directorate behind

185

a unanimous plan of action. Nor was there a Lyman Stewart in this emergency with the financial power to dictate a program. Instead, there evolved four schools, each with a different remedy for the ails of the battle-scarred veteran of the disastrous economic struggle.

The St. Clair school, backing the veteran president who had weathered the depression by cutting expenses to the bone and maintaining the dividend record, believed that time and tightening the belt would eventually bring the company out of its difficulties. It was the *status quo* school.

The so-called Matthews faction was headed by Executive Vice-president R. D. Matthews. Born and educated in Wales, Matthews had been appointed comptroller by John W. Garrigues in the great shake-up of 1913, and shortly afterward, at the age of twenty-seven, was elected to the executive committee, at which time he was Union's youngest director. Though a Garrigues appointee, he revealed independence by voting a year later to investigate Garrigues's expenditures. After modernizing Union's accounting practices, Matthews was put first in charge of manufacturing operations, then distribution. After he became executive vice-president during the St. Clair regime, Matthews developed a Garrigues flair for high-handed operation, frequently ignoring the president and the executive committee completely. This was resented by his associates, and created an atmosphere of dissension. It also doomed Matthew's ambition to become president.

The third school placed its hopes on W. L. Stewart, Jr., and Arthur C. Stewart, both of whom had climbed during the depression to positions of influence. Bill Stewart, with his chemical-engineering training, believed that the answer to Union's financial troubles was to extract more valuable products from each barrel of oil, a program that involved a heavy investment in laboratories and up-to-date refinery equipment. Art Stewart, like his father and grandfather, was a driving salesman who was sure Union could market at better prices to sell more of the products that Bill proposed to refine. Though the Stewart family was in no position to control the company, and made no attempt to do so, hundreds of old-time stockholders who had fared well under the Stewart dynasty were for giving the hard-working third generation of Stewarts an opportunity to show what it could do.

Differences between the opposing schools grew more acute early in 1938, when, following a serious automobile accident, President St. Clair announced his intention of retiring. The St. Clair proponents were in no mood to concede Matthews the presidency and the Matthews clan would not agree on a "St. Clair man" to head the company. Nor would the two groups bury their differences and agree to back another Stewart administration, which many of the stockholders wanted.

The way out of the impasse was found by a group known as the "outside directors," businessmen on the board as distinguished from directors who were on the Union payroll as executives of departments. In several informal off-the-record meetings, the "outside directors" can-

*Among famous wells of the west is Amerada King No. 1 in the North Dome of Kettleman Hills. Well was completed by Union Oil in July, 1931, at 8,310 feet for 20,000 barrels a day.*

vassed the field for a president behind whom all of the company's directors, stockholders, and employees could unite wholeheartedly. To nearly everybody's surprise, they found him sitting at the directors' table. He was husky, towering Reese H. Taylor, who had been elected to the board the year before, with the support of all of the groups. When the "outside directors" proposed Taylor for president, the St. Clair faction and the Stewart group accepted the idea with enthusiasm; the Matthews clan vigorously opposed it. Taylor was elected president in October, 1938.

Taylor's choice as president surprised nearly everybody, including the new boss of Union himself. Born in Los Angeles on July 6, 1900, Taylor had grown up in the iron and steel business. His father had been one of the founders of the Llewellyn Iron Works, in which young Reese, after

a mechanical-engineering training at California and Cornell, worked up to superintendent and director by 1925. When Llewellyn Iron was merged with the Union Iron Works, the Baker Iron Works, and the Gallagher Steel Company to form the Consolidated Steel Corporation, largest independent steel fabricating plant in Southern California, Taylor became production manager, then executive vice-president, and finally president in 1934. His selling feats during the depression years were legend in the Western steel business. When siphons too big to be transported by rail from the East were needed for the Metropolitan Aqueduct, Taylor contracted to fabricate them in Los Angeles and deliver them by truck and trailer, a feat that required clearing entire highways of traffic to make way for the big tubes. When Easterners thought they had all the steel fabrication for the

*W. L. Stewart, Jr., executive vice-president of Union Oil Company of California.*

Hoover Dam power-transmission towers sewed up, Taylor invaded the job and came away with a big slice of the contract for Consolidated Steel by selling some new engineering ideas along with his steel.

The oil game intrigued him because it was a basic Western industry, whereas steel fabrication was a branch of an Eastern industry. When Union's directors invited him to fill a gap at the table left by the death of Banker Henry M. Robinson, Taylor accepted in a hurry. A year later, when they invited him to be president, he asked time to think it over. While he made up his mind, he made sure that there were no strings to the job. The only resistance to his ideas for rejuvenating the depression-scarred company came from the Matthews camp. Taylor assumed office on

October 24, 1938. Ignoring the new president as he had the old, Matthews continued to take his ideas directly to the directors. Taylor called Matthews in, invited him to retire, which he did early in 1939. The Matthews faction evaporated, and once more Union's destiny was in the hands of a well-oiled management team.

Reese Taylor's impact on the moribund company was little short of atomic. Union expanded in every direction simultaneously. The one department in which Union had kept pace was in crude sources. The company had 1,200 producing wells, but nearly half of them were shut down. To produce 7 per cent of the Pacific Coast oil industry's gasoline, Union's refineries had to run 13 per cent of the Coast's crude. Union's refineries were twice as old and half as efficient as those of major competitors. A Chase National Bank analysis of 30 oil companies showed an average net investment of 16.6 per cent in refinery equipment; Union's investment in refining facilities was 8.3 per cent. Union had deteriorated to the position of a fuel and gas merchant, selling the cheap petroleum products, while better equipped competitors marketed the more profitable products.

Taylor's answer to this challenge was a 73 million dollar building program, equipping Union Oil with refineries and laboratories as efficient as any in the industry. The yield of gasoline from a barrel of oil shot up from 20 to 36 per cent, a large percentage being premium gasoline

for which there was an increasing demand at Union service stations.

Looking over the transportation picture, Taylor discovered that the tanker fleet consisted of 11 slow, overworked ships, the youngest of which had been in service fourteen years. The new management earmarked 15 million dollars for seven modern high-speed tankers, and 7 millions more for pipeline and tank truck equipment. Two of the new tankers were in service by the time World War II broke out, and the others were delivered soon after, enabling Union not only to play a leading role in fueling the armed forces but to dispose of the obsolete tankers to a ship-hungry market at half what they had cost originally. On top of this, the revitalized management poured 22 million dollars into better service stations, bulk-products depots, and marketing facilities. In the first decade of Taylor's leadership, Union spent more than 230 million dollars hunting and producing oil in 16 states, Alaska, and Canada, and rebuilding facilities for handling the crude, turning it into 400 products and marketing them.

This was more than Union's total capital value when Taylor became president. Raising the millions to streamline the company and launch it on its second half century called for some money raising that would have delighted the heart of

R. D. Matthews's ambition to become president was defeated by his high-handed acts.

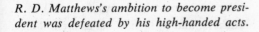

189

Lyman Stewart. A good share of the new money came out of greater earnings from more and better products, as Union's sales more than doubled in a decade to $208,985,000 in 1948. The company launched a drive to bring in more capital from investors on the Pacific Coast, particularly the Pacific Northwest. It sold $24,500,000 worth of preferred stock without difficulty. The number of shareholders increased fourfold to 35,000. By new financing, the funded debt increased $36,000,000 in ten years. This was only a beginning. In 1949, the company borrowed $40,000,000 more and issued 600,000 additional shares of stock to retire old debts and acquire the tremendous oil holdings of the heirs of Edward L. Doheny, thus adding 4,500,000 barrels a year to Union's production, and increasing the company's reserves by more than 48,000,000 barrels. The Union policy is still to maintain its major reserves inside the United States, preferably in the West.

"The backbone of Union's crude supply always has been and still is California," said Taylor as the company completed its sixtieth year in 1950. "In Union's search for new sources of natural petroleum, we are directing our efforts along three lines: first, deepening and extending existing fields; second, searching for new fields in areas not already developed, such as offshore drilling and wildcat drilling in new areas; third, recovering greater amounts of crude from existing fields than current production methods will yield. In unproved territory we are putting in more exploration than ever before in the company's history. We have crews working in a dozen states, in Canada and Alaska,

plus our offshore seismograph work in California coastal waters and the Gulf of Mexico. Some authorities think this offshore area is the greatest potential source of new oil in the country."

Along with this streamlining of production, transportation, manufacturing, and marketing, another evolution was keeping pace, namely, the streamlining of human relations. Union Oil was not only 2,000 oil wells pumping from 588 million barrels of reserves, plus pipelines, refineries, tank ships, tank trucks, depots, and service stations; it was 5,000 dealers plus 500,000 customers and 35,000 stockholders, in addition to hundreds of free-enterprisers whom the company had set up in independent businesses with service contracts; finally, it was 7,200 "Union Oilers," as the company's employees call themselves.

Union's human-relations program was launched by Will Stewart back in 1915, when the Employees' Benefit Plan was set up to provide medical care and hospitalization at cost. At that time, the company took out a 3-million-dollar life insurance policy covering its employees in a deal that was hailed as "the largest amount of life insurance ever negotiated in a single transaction west of the Missouri River." Out of this beginning evolved a modern program of medical care, sick pay, life insurance, termination allowance, and other features that J. P. Rockfellow, manager of employee relations, calls "as fine a protective ring as any group of employees could find anywhere."

Founder Lyman Stewart displayed a paternal interest in the welfare of Union workers, and in their souls as well. Three

190

generations later, Union's management had completely outgrown paternalism. Since 1930, the Employees' Benefit Plan, the medical care and health program, has been operated by a board of six administrators elected by the employees. The company's management has no veto over their decisions. In addition, through the Provident Fund, launched by W. L. Stewart during his presidency and now administered by the Equitable Life Assurance Society, Union provides pensions for retired Union Oilers.

The management's philosophy is that Union's employees are partners in Union's Black Bonanza along with Union stockholders, Union dealers, and even Union customers. This is a big bill of goods to sell, and, under Taylor's driving, Union's story and philosophy of business are repeated over and over in unique educational programs, by printed word, motion picture, road shows, and even television.

"Employees are entitled to know all about the company they work for," explains Taylor, by way of justifying Union's heavy expenditures in this field. "The way to make an employee realize he is a partner in the business is to keep him informed of decisions, policies and problems of management and seek his opinions and suggestions. Everybody working for Union is entitled to know how well the management does its job, where the money comes from, how it is used, how the earnings are distributed. Aside from trade secrets, what a company feels it can or it cannot explain to its employees, its customers, its stockholders, and the public in general is a pretty good indication of just how well it is being run. It takes more than money and material to make good products. Without an interested and informed public—customers, shareholders, dealers, and employees alike—there would be no Union Oil Company of California."

191

192

# CHAPTER ELEVEN

# Mud-smellers, Rock-hunters, and Earth-shakers

FROM a century of oil hunting, oil men have learned that oil is anywhere you find it. Sometimes it is under stream beds, sometimes under flat plains. It may be under hills, mountains, marshes, or under the sea. It has been found under cities, tropical jungles, arctic wastes. Oil hunters are convinced that more oil lies undiscovered in hidden geologic traps beneath the earth's surface than they have found in their hundred-year probe of the globe for more petroleum.

The problem is to locate these traps without spending more on exploration than the oil is worth. Oil hunting has advanced in a hundred years from the by-guess-and-by-gosh punching of shallow wells to an intricate science that sometimes means betting a million dollars on a single hole. Even the wizardry of costly scientific instruments can't tell if there is oil in the trap a mile or two below the earth's surface. All that science can do is detect a potential trap, which may contain oil or may not, as only a costly hole will reveal.

Oil hunting has already gone through three periods, those of the mud-smellers, the rock-hunters, and the earth-shakers. The mud-smellers sniffed out the oil seeps, like those of the Venango Valley in Pennsylvania, where Lyman Stewart made his first fortune, and of Pico Canyon and Adams Canyon in California, where he and Wallace Hardison eventually hit their stride.

Some mud-smellers eventually developed the nose for oil to a point where they could smell it without a seep or any other external sign of hidden petroleum. One of the greatest of these was Lyman Stewart, who picked up hundreds of thousands

*Union geologists use airplanes, ships, automobiles—and Old Dobbin in rough country.*

*A. C. Rubel, vice-president for production and exploration, Union Oil of California.*

of acres of grazing land at bargain prices. Though there were no seeps to indicate oil, and little geological survey to support his hunches, the pools of oil were down there, as drilling proved. Union's scientifically trained modern oil hunters still marvel at Lyman Stewart's uncanny nose for oil.

"We still don't know what the subsurface world is and what it contains," says A. C. Rubel, Union's vice-president in charge of exploration and production.

"Union's greatest asset is the acreage taken up by the old-timers, particularly Lyman Stewart. The lands he secured are still the backbone of the company's production. The La Habra Heights area alone, which he picked up for a song, may eventually yield fifty million barrels of oil. The hundred thousand acres in the Lompoc, Purissima, and Santa Maria areas he bought at farm prices may return even more. These were just rolling hills without a sign of oil traps beneath them. After over four decades of production, they are still valuable reserves."

Arthur Chatfield Rubel, who is plain "Cy" Rubel to oil people both in and out of the Union fold, typifies the evolution in oil hunting from mud-smelling to rock-hunting to earth-shaking. Born in Louisville, Kentucky, trained in mining engineering at the University of Arizona, Rubel emerged from World War I with a distinguished military record, just as the rock-hunters were in their heyday. Rubel spent four years in Mexico, Guatemala, and Honduras in geological and timber exploration. On one trip he was out of touch with civilization and his family for a year. In 1923, hearing that Union was launching a petroleum-engineering department, Rubel applied for a job. With Union, Rubel ran the gamut of field-work exploration, replacing the hit-or-miss methods of drilling with scientific engineering principles, keeping accurate and detailed record, reducing the guesswork in petroleum hunting. By the time he emerged in 1939 as vice-president in charge of Union's exploration and production activities, Rubel had a firsthand understanding of the problems of probing for oil. Most of all, he appreciated the doctrine laid down by Lyman Stewart that for every dollar paid in dividends the company should spend at least two finding more oil for future reserves. This policy, more than anything else, accounts for Union's steady sixty-year growth through the industry's alternate periods of famine and feast.

The 10 million dollars set aside each year in Union's budget for prospecting is five times as much as the whole company was worth when it grew out of the merger of three little oil companies in 1890. Even then, the founders sensed the need for a more scientific approach to probing for oil pools hidden under the jumbled surface of California. The upended mountains and twisted valleys presented a far more intricate geology than anything they had encountered in Pennsylvania. So they decided to locate new wells only after

*An anticline or rock upthrust in the Little Sespe district near Santa Paula. In its simplest form the anticline is a dome caused by the upfolding of rock strata. Early oil seekers drilled near seepages, later began looking about for telltale anticlines.*

195

*W. W. Orcutt, early geologist for Union Oil,*
*who later became vice-president of company.*

*Chester W. Brown, pioneer driller, and for*
*years in charge of Union's explorations.*

careful analysis of faults, dips, and out-croppings which indicated oil-trapping rock structure down below.

John Irwin, a practical field man with drilling experience in both Pennsylvania and California, and a nephew of Lyman Stewart, was assigned to study Western geology and develop a pattern for drilling. Irwin had to start from scratch, piecing together the geological story from logs of wells already drilled and from observation of faults in the Southern California hills and mountains. Thus John Irwin ushered in the era of the rock-hunters, or field geologists.

Although Irwin had to make a fresh

start in California, observers elsewhere had already learned something about the way nature cached petroleum deposits. They had hit on the so-called anticlinal theory of structural traps. In areas where porous rock strata of the earth had been folded, the oil and gas collected in the crests of the anticlines on top of the water pushing up from the adjoining troughlike synclines. If the rocks were free of water, then the oil lay in the bottom of the syncline, or lowest portion of the porous bed. There were other kinds of traps, too, such as the flanks of salt domes and faults, but the anticline was the easiest type to spot. Between John Irwin's rock-hunting

*Entire summit of hill in Cat Canyon leveled off for well site. After well was drilled and came*
*into production, the steel derrick was removed. Oil runs into tanks at base of hill.*

and Lyman Stewart's nose for oil, Union had uncanny luck in locating holes that tapped hidden oil pools in the Santa Paula area.

A decade after Irwin made this start at scientific oil-well locating, Lyman Stewart instructed W. W. Orcutt to organize the first fullfledged petroleum geology department established by a Western oil company. Orcutt, a Santa Paula youth who had done odd jobs around the Union refinery, then studied geology and engineering at Stanford University, was hired in 1898 not as a geologist but as a district land manager. Bill Orcutt has been called the "father of oil geology," probably more than his due, because geologists were already wrangling about petroleum traps before he was born. But

Orcutt did become the West's first outstanding oil geologist and an authority who strove to make petroleum geology a science instead of a guessing game. Probably Orcutt's great contribution, more important even than the new fields he helped discover, was the inspiration, guidance, and encouragement he gave to youthful geologists who later became the topflight oil hunters of the West.

Orcutt's insatiable curiosity led him to probe into the brea tar pits west of Los Angeles, alongside which Lyman Stewart and Dan McFarland had drilled their unsuccessful wildcat well in 1888. He had to know why they failed to hit oil when asphalt was oozing out of the ground. In the course of his scouting, he noticed on the surface of the pool of asphalt a mosaic

of white bones, uniform in shape and lying in a pattern, but resembling no animal he had ever seen. Orcutt had discovered the skeleton of an extinct giant ground sloth, an armored animal that roamed the earth millions of years ago. Embedded in the asphalt were skulls and skeletons of other ancient animals. Orcutt's find electrified the highbrow scientific world quite as much as an ocean of petroleum would have stampeded oil hunters. G. Allen Hancock, owner of the brea beds, assigned sections of the pits to a dozen different universities and museums for scientific exploration, and in a short time some 300 complete skeletons of saber-toothed tigers, giant mastodons, elephants, bisons, horses, wolves, condors, and innumerable smaller animals were recovered and pieced together—the richest paleontology bonanza found to date.

Bill Orcutt's early geological survey parties, the last word in their day, consisted of a spring wagon drawn by two horses, broken for saddle in case the terrain got too rough for wheels, bearing a grub box, blankets, a Brunton compass, picks, maps, a bale of hay, a sack of grain, a water bucket, a 10-gallon water keg, and a canvas canteen normally filled with water diluted with something stronger. The oil hunters always carried a few extra sides of bacon, because bacon was highly prized by the Basque sheepherders with whom the field geologists invariably camped at night. The sheepherders knew if there were any oil seeps or unusual outcroppings of rock in the neighborhood. Their tips led the rock-hunters to various remote sites, such as Bell Ridge, Buena Vista, and Lost Hills, which later became famous oil fields.

*Drilling in Dominguez Field calls for heavy equipment such as this five-ton assembly.*

*Field crew clamps elevators or "tongs" onto length of drill pipe to pull it out of hole.*

The bright and eager young geologists, fresh out of college with their ideas gleaned from books, were a pain in the neck to the old-time Pennsylvania and Ohio oil hunters who were witching the California hills with willow wands and bailing-wire "doodlebugs." The young geologists drew maps of the earth beneath the surface, guesswork maps projected from the upthrusts and the strata revealed in faults, particularly at the edge of valleys. What was important, they spotted new oil deposits successfully, better oil that was deeper down.

Where the old-timers set up rigs and

*Some wells produce hydrogen sulphide along with oil, so absorption plants such as this one at Santa Maria take in "dirty" crude at one end and send it out "clean" at other.*

drilled blindly, keeping only sketchy records of the rock formations through which they punched holes, the new geologists wanted foot-by-foot samples of the hole. An ingenious field man came up with an idea for a coring barrel, which cut out solid chunks of the hole, like saving the hole of a doughnut. Under a microscope, the geologists could readily tell from this core whether the drill was in coarse or fine sands, clays, shales, limestones, or conglomerates, and often they spotted fossil fish scales, marine life, wood fragments, or vegetable growth.

From this grew a new science, micropaleontology, the study and classification of microscopic fossils brought up in the rock borings. Some of these marine fossils were so unbelievably minute that they remained intact even after the core was reduced to a powder. Since oil was supposed to come from deposits of astronomical billions of microscopic organisms, the type of shells or fossils found in the core assumed new significance. Experience had already shown that good oil sites were there in areas in which marine life abounded millions of years ago. Gradually, the rock-hunters filled in many answers to the riddle: "Why is petroleum where you find it?"

World War I perfected two unexpected new weapons for the oil men. One was aerial photography. It is hard for the layman to understand how pictures made from several thousand feet up in the air would help the geologist tell something about the earth's formations several thousand feet below the surface of the soil. The answer is that photos from the air show upthrusts and other keys to the terrain hidden below. In 1919 Union employed Lieutenants Robert E. Haynes and Ralph M. Light, who had done aerial work for the AEF in France, to map first the Richfield district and later the Santa Fe Springs field.

The four hundred photographs they made covering 6,250 acres were so revealing that A. E. Fowks, assistant director of exploration, urged the company to buy a plane of its own. Union's management thought the idea was pretty fantastic. Fowks was ahead of his time. It wasn't long until Union and other oil companies were flying repaired tools to drillers, delivering them in an hour when a two-day trip by trucks would have been necessary earlier. Instead of one plane, Union operated a fleet of them, not only for exploration and emergency deliveries but to "ride pipeline," to rush lease makers and salesmen long distances. Planes made it possible to prospect in Paraguay, where there were no roads in the wildcatting area. Union's first wildcat location was on one of the battlefields of the Gran Chaco War between Paraguay and Bolivia. Amidst the machine-gun and ammunition

*Union uses floating derricks in drilling for gas and oil in spacious bayous of Louisiana.*

dumps, oil hunters found an abandoned airstrip which was easily cleared. A two-engine transport flew men, equipment, and supplies to the site of the drilling in less than two hours, covering distances that took five days on the ground in good weather, or three weeks during the rainy season.

The other new weapon was seismic or geophysical survey. Oil hunters had toyed with the idea of using miniature earthquakes to measure the distance down to hidden rock structures, even before the war. For World War I battlefields, both

201

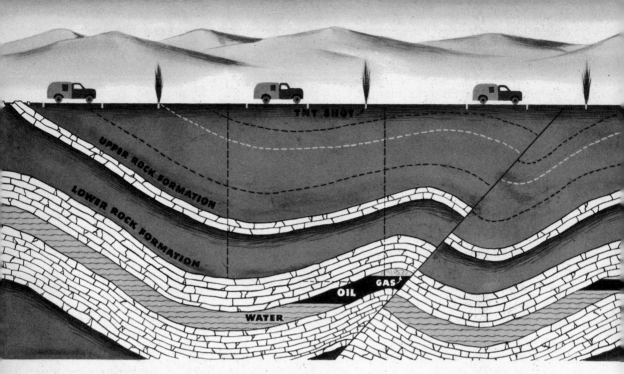

Reasonably accurate mapping can be done with a seismograph, but no scientific method can yet determine specific location of stratigraphic traps. Above: TNT shots are exploded at regular intervals to give geologists accurate data on depths and angles of various rock formations so that profile of subsurface can be drawn. Lower right: center segment of upper diagram shows TNT quake waves rebounding into surface geophones and being electrically recorded (left) as series of wriggly lines.

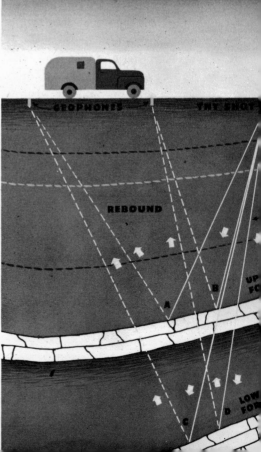

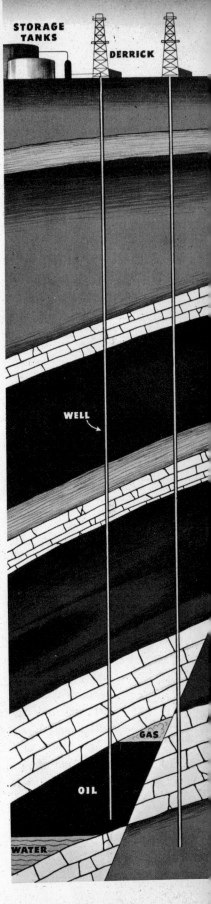

Top: TNT shot exploding in desert hurls up geyser of sand; below: a more spectacular geyser results from offshore seismic explorations when TNT is set off beneath the sea.

Right: "Only the bit can find oil." Diagram illustrates how one well may go down two to four miles and strike oil trapped by a fault, while its close neighbor, equally costly, misses both gas and oil.

the Germans and the Americans had evolved electronic gadgets for measuring sound waves set in motion by hidden artillery on the other side of no man's land. Thus a number of men were trained in the new science of seismic measurement.

When the war was over, these seismic experts found jobs in Texas and California working for the oil hunters. In Texas, the oil companies wanted them to find hidden oil domes, because the oil hunters had unusually good luck in finding pools of petroleum trapped around these subterranean mountains of salt. The seismic

sharks soon became known as earth-shooters or earth-shakers, thus launching the oil hunt on its third and most scientific phase.

To make their measurements, the seismic or geophysical survey crews drilled shallow holes with miniature drilling rigs set up on the tail ends of trucks. Then they dropped a charge of TNT in the hole, spread a network of geophones, or listening devices, for hundreds of feet around the hole, moved off a distance and set off the charge by pushing down the plunger in an electric firing box. The earth rumbled and shook, a geyser of mud shot skyward, and a miniature man-made earthquake vibrated downward. Whenever the quake hit a layer of rock, it bounced back, tickling the geophones which promptly reported the impulse by wire to an electronic recording machine on the sound truck. The recorder took a picture of the quake in wiggly lines on photographic paper, and when the pictures were developed they showed faintly wiggling lines for soft earth structures, medium wiggles for limestone and half-hard formations, and violently wiggled lines for the hard-rock areas. More important, they enabled the geophysicists to measure the depth of these formations by calculating the time it took the quakes to bounce back from different structures. Another help in sizing up the formations down as deep as two miles into the bowels of the earth was that the seismic waves traveled faster in soft formations than in the hard. This, too, was revealed by the wiggly lines on the long strip of photographic paper.

Shooting the earth was comparatively simple, and before many years passed, much of the North American continent had been shaken and photographed by hundreds of seismic crews. Some American earth-shooting crews quaked the earth from the Arctic Circle to Tierra del Fuego, and from the Philippines to the deserts of Arabia. Making effective use of the sur-

*Oil seeping from earth in rivulets such as this near Ojai pointed way to hidden treasure.*

*Geologist takes core samples from wells to determine formation bit has drilled through.*

veys was something else again, because the earthquakers' pictures didn't tell whether or not there was oil down below. They merely told where oil could be trapped.

"You've got to have a smart cookie who can interpret the wiggly lines," as Ed Schempf, director of some of the United Geophysical Company's seismic crews which worked for Union Oil, put it. Earthshooting quickly became a specialists' game. Union, like other oil companies, preferred to contract with seismic survey experts, who trained and directed their own crews. Interpreting the seismic pictures of California's heavily faulted subterranean structure proved far more difficult than that of the lower Mississippi Valley, where the earthshooters' activities inspired drilling that brought in phenomenal oil fields whose existence was indicated by no evidence that either the mud-smellers or the rock-hunters could possibly find.

Probably the most remarkable work of the earthquakers has been their work at sea. One of California's earliest oil fields at Summerland was under the surf. In exploring to round out several other basins, drillers worked from platforms in shallow sea water, and the Long Beach field was almost entirely under once-submerged tidelands dredged to make the city's harbor, a project financed largely by the Union Oil Company for many years. Unfortunately, in the preshooting days, Union's geologists had no reason to suspect they were dredging channels and building docks over what later became the state's richest single petroleum deposit.

Determined not to be caught uninformed again, Union joined two other oil companies, Shell and Continental, in a geophysical survey of the underseas continental shelf lying between the shoreline and the islands off the California coast. This is undoubtedly the most ambitious and complicated earthshooting yet attempted. Seismic crews have shot the swamps of the Louisiana bayou country, the shallow waters of the Gulf of Mexico, and the Arabian Sea, leading to rich oil discoveries, but never before have oil companies seriously contemplated finding and recovering oil in deep water, swept by currents and tides.

In the choppy Santa Barbara Channel, the earthshooters took to sea in an improvised mosquito fleet, consisting of two former Navy tenders and speed launches, bearing upwards of forty men. Before they could shoot the ocean, the seagoing earthquakers had to clear with the California Fish and Game Commission and promise to recover any dynamited fish and deliver

206

them to charitable institutions. They had to survey the restless ocean, to get their shot points and geophone locations in exactly the right spot on the maps they made with the aid of visual surveys from "fix points" on the shore. On foggy days, they had to rely on SHORAN, short-range radio navigation, perfected to help aviators find themselves in the clouds and fog above them. The earthshooting crews bobbed about until storms or high waves drove them ashore. The "smart cookies" who interpreted their pictures set up drafting boards in the nearest seacoast town with a wharf to which the speedboats could deliver the rolls of pictures of wiggly lines every evening.

The oil hunters are convinced that beneath the sea and the continental shelf off California is one of the richest undiscovered Black Bonanzas. "You've got to get away from the idea that there is any particular significance to a shoreline, geologically speaking, when you are hunting for oil," one of them explained. But ironically, even if they knew the oil was there, the oil hunters couldn't get it. One reason is that no one has figured out how to drill in shifting tides, even from huge floating barges, such as are used in the quieter waters of the Gulf of Mexico. The other is that a decision of the United States Supreme Court in 1947 transferred jurisdiction of the tidelands from the state to the Federal government, a decision that makes drilling for underseas oil a double gamble until Congress enacts legislation clarifying who can issue drilling permits.

One other almost magic device came out of World War II, to aid oil scouts in their probe for potential oil traps. This

Core samples from well are pulverized, then studied under microscope to check contents.

was MAD, the magnetic air-borne detector used by search planes to spot submerged submarines. Though MAD works on a different principle from seismic survey, its delicate instruments also detect impulses bounced back from solid formations. In time, MAD may be perfected into an "electric eye" that will make at least preliminary surveys of formations beneath the ocean's floor speedier and less expensively than costly oceanic earthquaking. On land, delicate gravity meters record the pull of solid-rock formations, enabling geologists to project outcroppings on down beneath the sediments. Another ingenious instrument, a "mechanical mudsmeller," even detects gas seeping through the surface soil in such minute quantities that an oil hunter's nose might miss it entirely.

The wizardry of scientific instruments has by no means put the old-fashioned hobnailed geologist or rock-hunter out of business. Sometimes the "smart cookies"

207

208

guess wrong, after studying the wiggly lines. An outstanding example of this was the greatest oil strike of recent years, the Cuyama Valley in Santa Barbara County. Petroleum geologists, including Union's, have looked at it for many years, wondering if there were petroleum deposits beneath the dry sands, hills, and bluffs. Four companies had sent earthshooters into the area and had decided Cuyama was a poor gamble.

Meantime, an old-fashioned hobnailed rock-hunting geologist named Tom Dibblee had been working over the area. Dibblee was the kind of rock-hunter that the modern scientific geologists had virtually counted out, after their fancy seismic instruments came into being. His methods were to go down into the hills and pick up upthrusts and project them down under the valley. On the basis of Dibblee's projected maps, the Richfield Oil Company decided that Cuyama Valley was "a sleeper" and put down several wells. They hit oil all over the valley at about 3,000 to 4,000 feet, making it one of the most sensational oil finds of the decade.

But for every sleeper like Tom Dibblee's find that they overlooked, the scientific oil hunters found a dozen new petroleum reservoirs that they might never have spotted without the benefit of seismic survey. Many older fields were rounded out

and extended as a result of these surveys, notably Signal Hill and Santa Fe Springs. In many cases it took a scientific map of the underground to give the geological and explorations departments courage to spend a quarter of a million dollars on a hole to tap the deep sands.

The mud-smellers, the rock-hunters, and the earthquakers have probed the subterranean earth under many and strange environments to add to the company's reserves of oil for future generations. They have found gassers in Wyoming, on the backbone of the Rockies, and more gassers 2 miles beneath the bayous of Louisiana, where wells can be reached only by launch and oil men live and work in houses built on barges floating on shallow waters. They have found oil under Texas, under Wyoming, under Alberta, Canada, where the earthshooters and drillers rigged up portable wintertime camps that even Eskimos would have envied; they have fought the jumbled geology and dense forests of the Olympic Peninsula for oil. They have wildcatted in Venezuela, Mexico, and on the pampas of Paraguay. Their most sensational strikes have been right at home, notably the discovery well of the high-pressure Richfield Field, that launched the billion-barrel, deep-well, high-gravity Los Angeles Basin oil scramble, a bonanza shared by scores of rivals. Or the Santa Fe Springs, the La

*Portable hoist at work in Union's Dominguez Field is called upon to lift immense weights as thousands of feet of sucker rods or steel tubing are brought to the surface. Its telescoping derrick and truck-mounted engines can be moved and set up in a matter of hours. Due to such rigs yesterday's forests of oil derricks are gradually disappearing.*

209

Habra Heights, the Rio Bravo, the Sansinena strikes, and a dozen others close to the Union pipeline network.

Altogether, Union's oil hunters have added up a grand total of 276,000 acres of proved oil area, plus some 3,000,000 unproved acres for the drillers to work on in the future. Yet the greatest potential reserve of all is up in the Rocky Mountains where, so far as the geologists know, there isn't any petroleum as such but where enormous beds of shale, laid down as the ancient inland seas receded, have locked in their strata vast quantities of oil by-products, including the makings of excellent fuel oil and gasoline.

Early in 1920, Union sent a scout into the Rockies in one of the strangest oil hunts in history. Many of the best shale deposits had been taken over by the Navy or preempted in mining claims. But Geologist R. H. Burnham, accompanied by A. S. Crossfield of the manufacturing department, had orders to survey Colorado to see if they could find the shale in a spot where it could be mined and refined economically.

"That was a terrific assignment," recalls Burnham. "The work was pioneering in every respect. There had been no detailed study by competent chemists and engineers, and there were no textbooks on costs of mining, retorting, or refining, nor, in fact, any assurance that a suitable oil could be obtained from the shale at anything like a reasonable cost. It called for a lot of hard work under dangerous conditions, fighting snow, ice, and falling rocks. Our entire outfit was packed into a single car. Crossfield had his retorts and chemicals apparatus fitted up to fasten on the running board of the car. That was the extent of our equipment."

Pete Lindauer, a colorful mountaineer, guided them to the shale ledges high above Parachute Creek. Pete pointed out almost unlimited shale beds, averaging 80 feet in depth. When they found a promising deposit, Crossfield ran a test on the spot, by cooking a batch of shale in a small portable retort with heat from a plumber's torch. He captured the vapor, ran it through a cool condensing pipe, and measured the resulting oil, in a sort of Rocky Mountain moonshiner's still. Sample after sample yielded oil in approximately the same amount—39 gallons of oil per ton of shale. Along with the oil there was invariably a considerable amount of combustible gas, which later investigation showed to be about 2,500 cubic feet of gas per ton of shale. The residue was a light, black material, incapable of producing more oil but usable as a low-grade fuel. With the oil, there was a small amount of water containing ammonia compounds useful for making fertilizers.

Samples of the shale sent to the Oleum laboratory confirmed Crossfield's findings with his moonshine outfit. These tests persuaded the Union directors that shale was the company's ace in the hole, if and when oil reserves ever ran out. They purchased in fee simple more than 20 square miles of a shale mountain near Rifle, Colorado. Later, they bought more. Cached in the Rockies, Union owns enough shale to produce 3 billion barrels of oil. That is ten times as much as Union owns in proved petroleum reserves.

210

## Man-made Rivers of Oil

MODERN civilization thrives on a global network of man-made rivers of oil which flow paradoxically over land and over sea to keep the machinery of today's living turning. These figurative rivers are seldom seen by the millions of humans dependent upon them. But if a stupendous earthquake or some other holocaust of atomic proportions were to cut the flow of these rivers of oil, so many planes, trains, trucks, busses, automobiles, factories, power plants, and heaters would come to a stop that a mechanized nation such as the United States would be paralyzed.

One of the first practical dreamers to vision these rivers of oil moving night and day through miles of pipeline was Lyman Stewart. As early as 1893, he was telling the directors of the infant Union Oil company of California, "With a 2-inch pipeline to San Pedro Harbor, we can reach the world with our products."

The directors were unimpressed, and not without reason. Stewart's idea of serving a world market was little short of ridiculous at the time. Union's 38 wells produced a total of 112,000 barrels of oil that year, just a little more than enough to fill a modern tanker. The San Pedro Harbor he referred to was a glorified mud flat, and no director could foresee that it would become before long a man-dug major Pacific Coast port, largely through Union's efforts and the company's urge to reach the markets of the world. Stewart and Hardison had already built the first pipeline to reach tidewater, from Santa Paula to Ventura, and the first tanker, too; but the tanker had burned, and without it the pipeline was of dubious value. Anyway, Union owned 55 tank cars and enough horse-drawn vehicles to haul the oil from the railroad yards to the customers' tanks. For these reasons, the directors persistently voted down Stewart's requests for money to lay a pipeline into the Los Angeles market.

Lyman Stewart bided time, until 1896, when Union's new wells in the Olinda oil field, not far from Los Angeles, became important producers. Then he laid a 4-inch line from Olinda to the city to compete with production in the overflowing Los Angeles field. Since the line had greater capacity than the production from Union's wells, he bought crude from other producers, pushed it through the pipe, showing a nice profit from the deal. In 1897, he extended the line to San Pedro, to deliver oil to ships. As the Los Angeles Basin and Orange County fields poured out their flood of oil, Union added miles of pipeline to handle the oil from the new

*Life to petroleum and its products is just one tank after another. This Torrance Tank Farm operated by Union Oil Company provides storage for 6,340,000 barrels of crude oil.*

wells. In a remarkably short time, Union had the beginning of the pipeline network connecting the oil fields with refineries, a system that grew into Union's Southern Division network, blanketing 1,000 square miles in the Los Angeles and Ventura Basins.

Then in 1904 the Hartnell gusher came in near Santa Maria, and Union had more oil from one well than all of its tank cars could handle by rail. Engineers rushed the building of a 33-mile pipeline from the Santa Maria, Lompoc, and Cat Canyon fields to tidewater at nearby Port San

*It is a lonely life for crews operating pumping stations such as this one at Middlewater in the "sand bowl" of San Joaquin valley, 15 miles north of Union's wells at McKittrick.*

Luis, which in 1909 became the terminus of the 8-inch, 30,000-barrel Producers Pipe Line from the San Joaquin Valley fields. Union was operating man-made rivers of oil in a big way. In one man's lifetime, the little 16-mile Santa Paula-tidewater line grew into a 1,200-mile system, with a capacity for 75 million barrels of oil a year.

The pipelines that handled this petroleum river were only the beginning. To push the sluggish oil on its way, about as fast as a man walks, called for 31 great pumping stations. The system handled dozens of kinds and grades of oil. Some of it so heavy that it had to be heated to 170 degrees to make it flow, then reheated at each pumping station. This called for a battery of heaters. Some of the crude was known as "wet oil." It came out of the well with so much water emulsified in it that it had to be dried, and this called for the building of a dozen big dehydrators, in or near the oil fields. Otherwise, much of the capacity of the pipeline and the pipes would be wasted pushing water over the hills to the refineries or the loading ports.

To store the oil handled by the pipeline system called for scores of huge tanks, some of them veritable man-made lakes of oil. When the steel tanks that are an integral part of Union's pipeline system were full, they accounted for 9 million barrels of oil. Another 13 million was stored in giant earth and concrete reservoirs, ranging in size from "The Baby"

at Kern River, holding a mere half million barrels, to "The Big Fellow" at Torrance with a capacity of 4 million barrels, the largest oil-storage lake in the world. Filling The Big Fellow was about like filling the largest football stadium in the world with oil from the gridiron to the press box. Altogether the pipeline department could account for almost 23 million barrels of oil, quite aside from whatever was flowing through the 1,200 miles of pipeline at the time.

This was only oil in transit. At the refineries huge steel tanks held another 9,750,000 barrels. The far-flung marketing depots soon had capacities for 4,791,000 barrels, and the tanks that stored the oil as it came out of the wells out in the fields held another 1,412,000 barrels. This gave Union a total storage capacity of 37,983,000 barrels.

The nightmare of oil men was, what would a fire do to these tanks and reservoirs? Union found out in 1926, when a storm swept in from the Pacific early on the morning of April 7, accompanied by dazzling flashes of lightning. At 7:53 A.M. three 1 million-barrel reservoirs at the San Luis Obispo tank farm were ignited simultaneously by the lightning strokes. Fifteen minutes later a second bolt hit an adjoining reservoir. After burning out of control for seventeen hours, the emulsified oil in the four reservoirs boiled over, igniting a fifth reservoir and a row of steel tanks. A few minutes later terrific whirlwinds struck the area, generated by the

*Union suffered one of the most spectacular and costly fires in petroleum history when lightning struck its San Luis Obispo tank-farm in 1926. Photo shows "boilover" of one 55,000-barrel unit with flames reaching miles skyward. Tank in center is 80 feet high.*

214

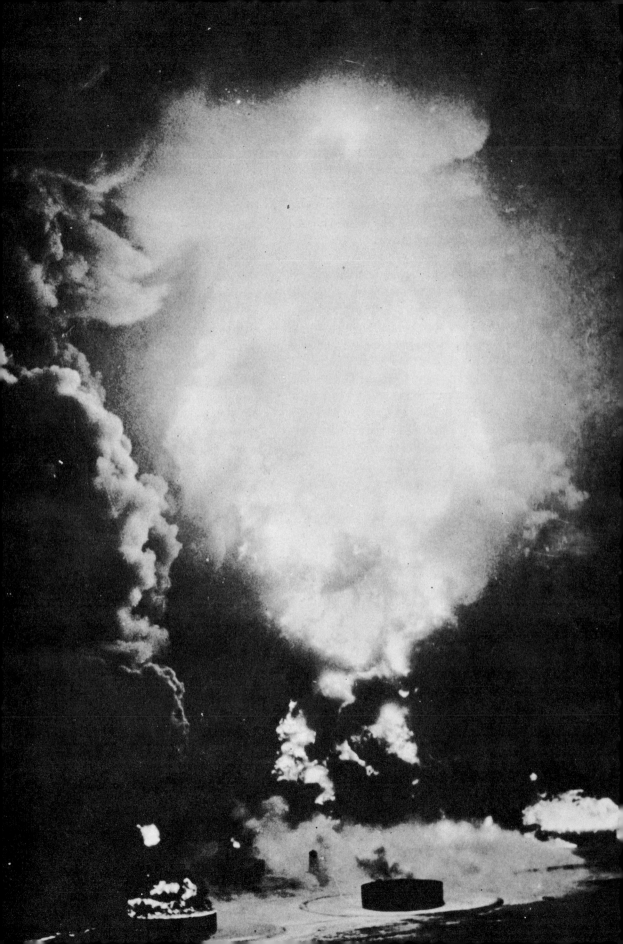

heat and aggravated by a 40-mile-an-hour gale blowing in from the southwest. Burning embers spattered on the roof of the sixth reservoir, set its 1,300,000 barrels afire. Other steel tanks were set aflame by the boiling over of the fifth and sixth reservoirs. Fifteen huge steel tanks crumpled under the terrific heat. The inferno burned for days, attracting greater crowds than a circus.

While this catastrophe was going on at San Luis Obispo, the storm moved south and east, hovering one day later over Union's great tank farm at Stewart, 1 mile west of the town of Brea in Orange County. At 9 A.M. on April 8, a bolt of lightning ignited two of the Stewart reservoirs simultaneously. When these boiled over, they ignited a third, and finally engulfed a small refinery in the lake of flaming oil. An army of three thousand men hurriedly recruited from nearby oil fields and refineries tossed up dykes that held the lake of fire. A fortnight later, when insurance underwriters were able to appraise the damage, they branded it the greatest fire loss since the San Francisco fire of 1906. Nearly 8 million barrels of oil were destroyed, plus 21 huge steel tanks, plus serious damage to reservoirs, innumerable pipeline fittings, and many pumps, not to mention damage to surrounding ranches. When the insurance adjusters finished their calculating, Union's treasurer received checks totaling more than 9 million dollars.

The great fire led to one of Union's unique operations, the "fire lab," which has specialized ever since in starting and quenching oil fires. The fire lab consists of metal tanks, pits, sheds, towers, vehicles, and other equipment, fired with various kinds of oils and gases, so that Union's fire fighters can study the habits of fires and practice putting them out. The fires they ignite are the real thing. Union's fire fighters have become so expert at battling oil conflagration that officials of several municipalities have arranged for their own firemen to take the training.

As pipelines became the arteries of the petroleum industry and as the oil flowing

*Union employees are trained to fight fire by attending class in this superhot laboratory.*

*Dispatcher watches "Board" of Union's southern pipeline division to check movement of hundreds of thousands of barrels of oil so they will not become mixed or misrouted.*

through them became the lifeblood of thousands of other industries, their operation became a complex skill, often baffling to the layman. Since nearly every field yielded a different kind of crude, the oil was pushed through in batches known as "tenders." Some of the products lines from the refineries soon were handling a dozen products, ranging from aviation gas to fuel oil, and tenders of these chased one another through the pipeline, like trains on a railroad, without getting mixed up. Some were pushed into the line at one pumping station, some at another, and the tenders were drawn off at various points—likewise without getting mixed up.

Keeping all these batches and kinds of oil moving through the unseen rivers became the job of a new czar in the oil industry, the pipeline dispatcher, and his assistants. By keeping his eye on "The Board," a map of the pipeline system with little brass pegs marking the hun-

dreds of valves along the line, and by consulting "the dope book," recording every day's movement of every tender of crude or products, the dispatcher kept the system working day and night. At every station, the end of one shipment was checked, sometimes by a shot of dye or a slug of fresh water or by a "go-devil," the latter being a round plug that scraped off wax and rust, polishing the inside of the pipeline to reduce friction.

Dials indicating pressure changes reported closed valves, line stoppages, or breaks in the line as it wound over the hills. In the early days, pipeline inspectors rode over the wastes, or walked, watching for breaks, but after World War II, the inspectors took to the air in slow-speed, low-flying planes, covering as many miles in a minute as the old-time inspector checked in a day. Along Union's Northern Division, the pipeline system north from

217

*Heavy hoses from four to sixteen inches in diameter are used to load Union's tanker fleet.*

Bakersfield and Santa Maria, Union's flying inspector spotted two hundred leaks in a single year from the air. Once, to check the flier's alertness, the superintendent of the system dumped 5 gallons of crude over the line at a remote point. Within an hour, the flier called in about the "break."

"And you left your oil can under a sagebrush on the west side of the line," he added.

The pipeline system solved only half of Lyman Stewart's dream of rivers of oil flowing to the markets of the world; the other half called for a fleet of tankers to keep the river flowing across the sea. But tankers were useless without harbors, and nowhere near the Southern California oil fields was there a natural harbor. The nearest excuse for one was at San Pedro, where a narrow channel had been dredged through the mud flats to some inadequate wharves.

In 1912, a young Navy engineer, Lieutenant Randolph H. Miner, advanced a big idea for dredging a huge basin behind

*Big and little tanks, twisting, turning pipes of all sizes and powerful pumps combine to enable Union's terminal facilities at Oleum Refinery to handle 150,000 barrels a day.*

219

the breakwater which the Federal government had completed. Lyman Stewart agreed to lease some of the waterfront acreage Miner proposed to create with mud from the basin. To get the harbor work started, Union took a one-twelfth interest in Miner's Outer Harbor Dock and Wharf Company. Miner soon ran into financial difficulties. To keep the work moving, Union advanced so much money that it finally had to take over the entire project. Wharf and industry sites were filled in with mud pumped from channels. Sea walls and wharves were built. It was a big bite of geography-making for one oil company.

The city of Los Angeles was becoming marine-minded, and the city counsel, anticipating completion of the Panama Canal, reached out for a harbor, annexing the little municipality of San Pedro lock, stock, and waterfront. San Pedro was hooked to Los Angeles by "The Shoestring," a strip of land 1 mile wide and 20 miles long. This feat of gerrymandering completed, the Los Angeles city officials undertook to oust Union Oil from the outer harbor property into which the company had been pouring hundreds of thousands of dollars. At the time the Outer Harbor project was about three-fourths complete.

The city fathers soon bumped into a wrathy Lyman Stewart. They filed a suit of ejectment to force Union from the lands it had created. Rarely given to anger, this aroused the full ire of Lyman Stewart. He slapped a legal action right back at Los Angeles, charging the city's action was "an unwarranted attempt to confiscate our property—property as justly and lawfully acquired as any property ever can

*At Avila, on the coast between Los Angeles and San Francisco, Union Oil pipelines bring crude over the mountains from inland fields to these tanks from which ships are filled.*

*Union Oil's marine terminal at San Pedro with the company's tremendous Los Angeles refinery in background. Terminal handles eight different commodities simultaneously.*

be," adding that "it is our firm determination to protect our rights at the ultimate latitude given us by the laws of the municipality, the commonwealth, and the nation."

"We have, in perfectly good faith, invested $1,600,000 in this enterprise," he told the city council. "This money is the property of 4,200 stockholders, the larger number of whom are residents and taxpayers of Los Angeles, and it seems inconceivable that the city administration would seek to deprive its own citizens of their justly acquired legal rights."

This vigorous stand took the city authorities by surprise. To avoid a long legal fight, they offered a compromise. Union would hold, under a thirty-year lease agreement, the acreage it had built and which the city agreed to purchase. Lyman Stewart accepted this offer, in an agreement signed April 4, 1922, and expiring on April 4, 1952, on which date the wharves, piers, channels, and bulkheads become the property of the board of harbor commissioners. Other structures, machinery, and installations remain the property of Union Oil. Meantime Union had purchased 260 acres for a refinery site near the harbor. Thus at last Stewart had the pipeline and harbor facilities he had visioned for Union Oil's growth.

By this time, Union had a tanker fleet, too. The Union fleet dates from 1900, eleven years after the "W. L. Hardison"

went up in flames, when the directors authorized construction of the "Santa Paula," a full-rigged schooner with a capacity of 8,200 barrels, to carry fuel to the Hawaiian Islands. Because the ship had to be built fast and cheap, the "Santa Paula" was a sailing schooner, to Lyman Stewart's chagrin. After the "Santa Paula" came the barkentine "Fullerton" in 1902, another sailing vessel with the then huge capacity of 16,000 barrels. In view of Lyman Stewart's aggressive crusade for oil to fuel ships, construction of the two sailing ships was something of an anachronism. So the next tanker, the "Whittier," was a steel-hulled steamer with a capacity of 11,000 barrels.

*Right: Oleum Refinery on San Francisco Bay sends products to market by truck, steel drums, railroad tank cars, barges, and tank ships. On left, steel drums of lubricating oil go aboard flatcars; on right, tank cars are being loaded, and ship is filling at end of dock.*

*Below: Motor transports load asphalt and fuel oil at Oleum Refinery for distant delivery.*

Union has operated rail tank cars for six decades and now has 650 modern cars such as this.

Barges carry asphalt and fuel oil to ports on San Francisco Bay and up Sacramento River.

The "Whittier" signaled a new era for tankers. Her engines were set aft to reduce the fire hazard. The cargo tanks were an integral part of the hull, giving the vessel greater stability in rough weather. In the bow was space for dry cargo. Galley and quarters for engineers and crew were likewise aft, with deck officers amidships, convenient to the bridge. The ship set a new pattern, for nearly every tanker built since that time has followed her basic design.

The "Whittier's" engines were more powerful than she needed, so Union's marine engineers soon found use for this extra horsepower. Sawing off the masts of the "Santa Paula," they converted the schooner into a barge which the "Whittier" pulled up and down the coast, virtually doubling the delivery capacity of Union's fleet. This operation worked so smoothly that in 1903, when a critical shortage of oil developed in Hawaii, the "Whittier" was dispatched to the Islands with the "Santa Paula" plus the "Fullerton" in tow. No such tandem-tow over 2,500 miles of open sea had been attempted before, and many a mariner thought it foolhardy. But the "Whittier" left California loaded down with 11,000 barrels, the "Santa Paula" with 8,200 barrels, and the "Fullerton" with another 16,000 barrels, the largest single cargo of oil sent to sea up to that time. In ten days she reached Honolulu; on the twenty-eighth day after her departure, the "Whittier" returned to California with the two barges still in tow—mission completed.

Following these pioneers came a distinguished line of seagoing oil carriers,

*Union tanker Lompoc, capacity of 140,000 barrels, loading at Oleum Refinery Terminal.*

*Tanker Santa Paula, second ship of this name to be operated by Union Oil, has capacity of 140,000 barrels. Original Santa Paula was schooner carrying 8,200 barrels.*

some of them ships that live in legend. One such was the "Santa Rita," the ship that ran into itself.

Hard pressed in 1909 for tankers to handle the crude pouring out of the new Producers pipeline at Port San Luis, the company contracted with the Newport News Shipbuilding Company to convert the "Santa Maria" and the "Santa Rita," sister ships built in 1902 for the Great Lakes trade, into tankers. To get them out of the Lakes through the locks and down to the sea, the ships were cut in two amidships. The stern of each ship towed its bow, the machinery being in the stern. The "Santa Maria" negotiated the locks all right, but the "Santa Rita" stopped too suddenly one day and the bow plowed

through the stern bulkheads. Luckily, the "Santa Rita" did not sink herself. Patched up, she reached the ocean. The ships, each capable of handling 55,000 barrels of oil, were ultimately lost in the Atlantic. Sold by Union at the outset of World War I, the "Santa Rita" foundered in high seas; the "Santa Maria" was torpedoed by a German submarine.

Fifteen years after Wallace Hardison had a tanker named for him, Union got around to honoring the other founder of the company with the "Lyman Stewart," a 65,000-barrel tanker launched in 1914. A sister ship, the "Frank H. Buck," was built for the Associated Oil Company at the same time on adjoining ways. In 1922 the "Lyman Stewart" collided at the en-

*Deeply laden tanker steams through heavy swells en route from Los Angeles to Honolulu over path first traversed by a Union ship a half century ago in opening up vast Pacific trade.*

trance of San Francisco Bay with another ship and sank. Fifteen years later the "Frank H. Buck" collided with the "President Coolidge" at the identical spot and sank within 50 feet of the "Lyman Stewart." There the ill-fated sisters still rest, side by side on the bottom.

Of the seven major ships in Union's service in 1950, four—the "L. P. St. Clair," "Victor H. Kelley," "Paul M. Gregg," and "A. C. Rubel"—have cargo capacities of 100,000 barrels. The newer "Santa Paula," "Oleum," and "Lompoc" are each equipped with 140,000 barrels of cargo-tank space. Even the largest tankers can load in twelve hours and discharge a full cargo in twenty-four hours. Hundreds of storage tanks strategically located from Nome, Alaska, to Valparaiso, Chile, and westward across the Pacific, are dependent upon these tankers for their share in the river of oil.

When World War II broke, December 7, 1941, Union's tanker fleet and its trained marine personnel were ready for action. The fleet of seven modern tankers were chartered immediately by the War Shipping Administration and, together with a score of government tankers, assigned back to the company for operation. Five Union tankers were already in the war, two carrying British oil between the Dutch West Indies and the Atlantic Coast; three more delivering petroleum products to Vladivostok, and to United States outposts in the Pacific.

Within the first two weeks of hostilities Union's fleet suffered its first tanker loss. The "Montebello," under command of Captain Otto Edstrom, had loaded at Avila with a cargo for Vancouver. She headed out to sea December 23, 1941, without escort. Two hours later, barely out of sight of land, a lurking Japanese submarine, which had started its journey to the Pacific Coast well before war had begun, sent a torpedo crashing into the port side of the tanker. Surfacing, the U-boat poured shells into the wallowing, smoking ship as the crew took to lifeboats. While the "Montebello" slid beneath the waves, the crew pulled for the shore under a rain of Japanese machinegun bullets, which miraculously failed to wound a single crewman.

Eleven months later came the tragic loss of the "Gurney E. Newlin," commanded by Captain Herman Dahllof, torpedoed without warning in mid-Atlantic. Only seven of the tanker's crew of 41 Union Oilers were saved.

Union tankers fed fuel to American ships during the invasion of Africa; they filled Navy bunkers from Australia to Guam to Saipan, Manila, and Okinawa, Iwo Jima, and on to Yokohama. They were on hand at the surrender in Tokyo Bay. Japanese naval strategy, based on the idea that ships had to return to bases for fuel as they had always done after battle in previous wars, was completely befuddled when American ships fought one battle, then kept on striking before the Japanese admirals were ready for the next fight. After the war, the Nipponese learned what kept them continuously off balance. It was a never-failing river of oil flowing across the Pacific from wells and pipelines of Union and other oil companies. The tankers were floating supply bases, pumping fuel into high-speed Navy tankers which, in turn, refueled the combat ships on the move. The tankers kept the never-failing river of fuel and gasoline flowing ashore at the islands on which the Air Force based their fighters and bombers. They fed the Army's tanks and trucks and bulldozers. This river of oil was so important that Admiral Chester W. Nimitz called it "one of our greatest secret weapons," when he sent personal citation to Union's tanker "La Placentia" for the outstanding work she did at Majuro Atoll in directly fueling combat ships.

After V-J Day the river of oil became once more a peacetime river, keeping the machinery of modern civilization spinning, in cities, on farms, on land and sea, and in the air.

# CHAPTER THIRTEEN

# What's in a Barrel of Oil

WHEN the Union Oil Company of California was born in 1890, the primitive Santa Paula refinery was able to extract four commercial products from a barrel of crude, namely, kerosene, fuel oil, grease, and asphalt. By 1950, when Union rounded out its sixtieth year, the petroleum industry had learned how to extract four thousand different products from a barrel of crude, and Union's two big refineries at Oleum and Los Angeles between them were making four hundred products.

This incredible increase in the useful yield of a barrel of oil becomes all the more remarkable when it is realized that many of today's more valuable products were a nuisance and waste when Lyman Stewart and Wallace Hardison first undertook to refine crude at Santa Paula by cooking it in horizontal brick stills resembling ovens. The cooking at low heat in the first oven got rid of the more volatile gases, unwanted and dangerous to handle, which were allowed to escape into the air. Thus the pioneers vaporized and

threw away what later became the company's No. 1 product in both quantity and value, gasoline, and cut out of the barrel of oil the part that put this country and much of the world on wheels.

The next oven, with a higher heat, cooked off the kerosene, the prize product of the day, except that kerosene from California crude was dark-colored and burned with bad odor and smoke. It was primarily to get rid of this stink and smoke that Lyman Stewart talked Union's directors into spending $2,500 for the West's first petroleum laboratory at the little Santa Paula refinery. The $2,500 was harder to raise than the 5 million dollars which Union's management invested in the magnificent petroleum laboratory at Brea six decades later. The difference between these two laboratories dramatizes the growth, not only of the Union Oil Company and the oil industry but of the whole conception of the potential of a barrel of oil.

A barrel of crude is regarded now by petroleum technologists as an almost bottomless storehouse of useful treasures.

*Original refinery of Union Oil at Santa Paula was built in 1887 when production of the Hardison & Stewart Oil Co. had reached 50,000 barrels a year. Plant was destroyed by fire 1896.*

*Los Angeles Refinery of Union Oil Company of California as it appeared in 1920.*

*Los Angeles Refinery in 1950 covers hundreds of acres alongside the harbor at San Pedro. Its 311 tanks, ranging in size from 138 barrels to giants of 133,889 barrels, can hold a total of nearly six million barrels, exclusive of water or chemicals.*

The four thousand products already found in it are only a starter. A barrel of oil is power, heat, shelter, plastics, synthetic fabrics, and rubber. It is refrigerant, medicine, pest control, preservative, pavement, explosives, to mention only a handful of its boons to man. Unlocking this storehouse is the job of the chemical engineers in the laboratories and the refineries.

Union's technologists have done their share, starting with the funny little $2,500 laboratory built at Santa Paula in 1890. Though Dr. Frederick Salathe, Union's first chemist, was employed primarily because he had developed a process for refining a water-white illuminant from pe-

troleum to compete with coal oil, it took so many years to lick the problem of making good kerosene from California crude that kerosene was no longer the big prize in this black liquid treasure trove.

Two other products that became the company's bread and butter emerged from the Santa Paula laboratory and refinery before it went up in flames in 1896. These were fuel oil, cooked out of the third stage in the horizontal ovens, and asphalt which was an end product. In this oil, with the water dehydrated out of it, Lyman Stewart had a product with which to revolutionize Western industry. In the asphalt, for road paving and roofing, he had one with which to invade the home

*This small refinery at Bakersfield processes some of the San Joaquin Valley production.*

fields of his big Eastern competitors, who found little or no asphalt in their paraffin-base crudes.

But the Pennsylvania oil producers had two articles which the California oil men needed desperately, clear kerosene and a wax-free paraffin-base lubricating oil. In the Oleum Refinery, completed luckily in 1895, before the Santa Paula plant burned, the company's technologists tackled the kerosene and lubricant problem with new vigor. They had larger facilities with which to work than at Santa Paula, but not much better. The original

Oleum plant, rated as the last word in refineries at the time, was still the horizontal oven type, a larger edition of Santa Paula. By comparison with the present-day Oleum or Los Angeles refineries, or even Union's smaller refineries at Bakersfield and Cutbank, Montana, it was primitive indeed and the hard way to unlock a barrel of oil. For a time, it produced so inefficiently that the directors considered selling it. Fortunately, in the era of John Baker, Jr., who took over responsibility for the refinery's operation as well as for selling its products, fuel-oil sales soared,

*Even blizzard approaching Cut Bank, Montana, refinery fails to slow operations.*

and, with increased output, efficiency improved. For the first time, Union's refining operations made money.

New products added to the returns. They illustrate how, in the ever-changing oil industry, one thing leads to another. One was gasoline, the volatile top gas formerly evaporated into the atmosphere. With the evolution of the automobile, gasoline loomed so valuable that Standard Oil, Union's most feared competitor, tried to tie up Union's entire output on contract, a proposition which Lyman Stewart shrewdly turned down, though at the time Union was refining gasoline only on order.

Another was grease, a product made by-guess-and-by-gosh and by the skill of Pete Nancett, who mixed petroleum lubricants with beef tallow and dye, stirred each vat of the stuff, then dipped up a sample on a barrel stave, tasted it, fingered it, and studied it as the grease cooled on the stave sticking out of the grease-room window. The "Nancett Analysis" gave way to even more scientific tests, which revealed that one revolutionary all-petroleum grease, Unoba, would do the lubri-

233

*Duo-Solvent Unit 220 at Oleum Refinery opened in 1950 to increase production of Triton.*

cating on automobiles and other machines that formerly called for five separate greases. Eventually grease research cut 45 lubricants from Union's list of products and added one new one capable of resisting even arctic or high-altitude temperatures.

Another outstanding by-product of the Union laboratory, as it grew in size and importance, was lubricating oil for the growing automobile, truck, and tractor fleets of the Pacific Coast. Western refineries were behind the eight ball in the lube field, because the crude from their wells

was full of wax and asphalt. Pennsylvania oil men made better oils from paraffin-base crudes. Here was a huge market going to competitors by default.

As Union technologists broke down the barrel of oil, they found that Western crude had paraffin in it, too. They also mastered the wax, after innumerable experiments, by treating the oil distillate from the refinery with propane, another by-product, which chilled and solidified the wax, after which it was filtered out of the oil. The outcome of this successful bit of unlocking was a brand-new motor oil,

234

so smooth and so resistant to oxidation that Union was not only able to compete with Pennsylvania oils in the West but to move into the Eastern field as well. Triton sales zoomed so steadily that the company had to spend over 11 million on additions to the Oleum refinery to make this one product alone.

Now for a look at those wax crystals, which were for so many years the nemesis of Western lubricant makers. When removed from the oil, they were dark, almost black, and unappetizing, but after being pushed through special filters, they emerged as white as sugar. Thus purified, the wax, eventually known as Aristowax, became one of Union's profitable by-products. Aristowax has many chores. It moistureproofs milk cartons; waxes paper to wrap bread; keeps barnacles off ship bottoms; sprayed hot on newly printed paper as it emerges from the presses, the wax keeps the color pages of the *Saturday Evening Post* from sticking together. Aristowax is another bright illustration of how one thing leads to another when chemists start unscrambling a barrel of oil.

What expedited this unscrambling was a series of radical new developments in refineries themselves. The first was the vertical still, in the form of the tall metal towers, characteristic of petroleum refineries. These fractionating towers, developed about 1911 and continuously improved during the next decade, made breaking down the barrel of oil a continuous process. Crude flowed into the highly heated bottoms of the towers in small rivers, and the cuts flowed out in vapors at various elevations. The cuts, or fractions, were usually five in number: gasoline distillates at the top, then the kerosene distillates, the stove oils, the gas or diesel oils, the lubricant distillates, and at the bottom, the heavy residuals which became bunker oils or furnace fuels.

Except for the residuals, each of these fractions could be broken apart and put together again, by utilizing revolutionary new refining processes, some so complicated they defy description in layman's

*Distillation Unit 67 at Oleum produces a number of products from Valley crudes.*

235

*Heart of the TCC Unit is this control center with its 200 operating instruments.*

language. Most of them came out of the urge to get more gasoline out of a barrel of oil. About 1910, gasoline passed kerosene as the No. 1 product extracted from crude. Gasoline was still only one-fifth of the barrel of oil, and refiners wanted more, and likewise gasoline with more wallop or octane rating. About 1913 experimenters began "cracking" the molecules in petroleum under high temperatures and high pressure, after which the fragments recombined in new molecules, some lighter and smaller than the original, some heavier and larger. This led to the fuming catalytic cracking columns, a fa-

miliar sight around modern refineries. Union's great "Cat Cracker" at Los Angeles towers 268 feet in the air, as high as a 20-story building. It "cracks" up to 60,000 barrels of crude a day and, more important, can convert up to 75 per cent of a barrel of crude into high-octane gasoline.

To the layman, the workings of the catalytic process are next to unbelievable. The work-horse in the Union "Cat Cracker" towers is a tiny gray porous clay pellet about the size of a pea. Millions of these pellets drop in a steady rain down the hot towers piling up twenty feet deep at

*Tremendous TCC Unit (Thermofor Catalytic Cracking) at Los Angeles refinery produces high-octane gasoline by using tiny clay pellets as effective catalysts.*

237

the bottom. As they fall, they contact gas vapors, which have reformed into new molecules. The vapors are drawn off for further processing into gasoline and a score of other products. The pellets flow out the bottom of the tower, covered with soot. They are then hoisted through a hot stream of air, which burns off the soot, restoring their reactivity qualities. After that they tumble again to pick up more gas vapors, making the round trip twenty times a day. The reason they can contact so much gas vapor so fast to make so much gasoline to fill so many automobile tanks is that between their exteriors and their porous interiors, the catalyst pellets are virtually all surface. The 15 million

*Natural gasoline sent into this Unit 91 at Los Angeles refinery is distilled under high pressure and separated into fuel gas, liquid petroleum gas, isobutane, and 7600 gasoline.*

pounds of pellets that drop in Union's big Los Angeles "Cat Cracker" during each twenty-four hours are estimated to have about as much surface as the state of California.

Another piece of refinery equipment whose work is pure wizardry is the "Bubble Tower," today's version of the fractionating tower. At the bottom the heat ranges up to 700 degrees. At the top the temperature is somewhat less, but still hot enough to vaporize the more volatile cuts in the barrel of oil. The crude flows into the hot bottom of the Bubble Tower, vaporizes, rises, is caught in the series of trays, bubbles over and drops to lower trays, and is drained off wherever the refiner wants to make his "cut." The Bubble Tower not only increased the potential cut of gasoline-making gases, but also speeded production and added flexibility to refining. If the customers demanded more gasoline, the refiner could cut out a larger fraction. If the market wanted diesel oil, he drew more of his barrel of oil out of the lower trays.

The technical advances in refining originated in many places. The first catalytic cracker grew out of the experiments of E. Houdry of France, who was trying to make synthetic oil from coal. It was adapted to petroleum by Dr. William M. Burton of Johns Hopkins, and improved upon by the technologists of many companies, including Union's. Probably Union's greatest contribution to the science of unscrambling petroleum's many ingredients is a process known as "hypersorption." This term, which had to be coined by its originators to describe superadsorption or the adherence of gases to solid

*Spherical steel tanks are used for storing isobutane, butane and very light gasolines.*

surfaces, is a brand-new one in the oil book. Hypersorption, one of chemistry's steps forward, grew out of the successful efforts of Dr. Clyde Berg, Union's supervisor of process development, and his staff to capture petroleum gases in a moving bed of activated charcoal.

The hypersorption process enables chemists to capture many gases that have hitherto been costly to harness. By this process they can recover at low cost the ethylene prevalent in gases generated by the catalytic cracking process. Ethylene puts "kick" in gasolines, is used in antifreeze, in plastics, and in many chemical manufacturing operations. Hypersorption makes possible the inexpensive capture of hydrogen, used to convert vegetable oils into margarine, to make ammonia for fertilizers, and to convert compounds into plastics. It also reduces the cost of recovering propane from natural gas, propane

239

*Hundreds of miles of pipe, big and little, weave intricate patterns in a refinery.*

being the chemical that solidifies the wax crystals in oil destined to become lubricants.

In fact, the products of hypersorption had so many chemical and pharmaceutical uses that it looked as though Union's new process was pushing the company into the chemical business. Instead, Union licensed several chemical manufacturers and, as an ironical side light to how one thing leads to another when technologists start juggling the ingredients of a barrel of oil, Union was thus scooped in the actual use of its own process.

This is a paradox which time will undoubtedly correct. At Union's hypersorption pilot plant at the Los Angeles refinery, researchers are trying the process for more economical recovery of gases and vapors that yield innumerable potential by-products. "The possibilities are almost unlimited," says Vice-president C. E. Swift, who is director of Union's research teams.

Headed by Dr. Clyde Berg, one of Union's teams is wrestling with what may be the biggest potential of all, recovering oil from shale. The company's vast shale holdings in the Colorado Rockies presented some unique problems. One was how to mine the shale economically. Another was how to coax the oil out of the shale without the use of water, since refineries are normally great users of steam and the shale deposits were in an area of little moisture. Third was the problem of converting shale oil into synthetic petroleum products. Shale oil isn't petroleum, but from it can be made many of the products the oil industry gets from petroleum crude, such as jet-engine fuel, diesel fuel, gasoline. It can be "cracked" into many hydrocarbon combinations, yielding other products. Shale oil is also rich in nitrogen and sulphur compounds, which must be removed by catalytic hydrogenation before the oil itself can be processed by normal refinery units. Mixed with the oil, the sulphur compounds are a stinking nuisance, but with their molecules adroitly juggled they can be processed into valuable amino acids, while the hydrogen has many uses such as converting vegetable oils, making fertilizers, plastics, ethyl alcohol. In fact, these and other by-products of shale oil may be worth more than oil itself as a source of fuel and power.

At Union's shale-oil pilot plant, Dr. Berg and Homer Reed, process engineer, have found the answers to most of the

*Gigantic oil storage tanks are placed on the hills back of Union's Oleum Refinery.*

problems of shale-oil recovery, except one, that is, how to produce it at a cost competitive with petroleum oil. The retort they have developed is an ingenious extractor that functions without water. A piston mechanism forces the shale up slowly through a vertical column, in which the spent shale is burned at the top to provide hot gases which sweat the oil out of the cold shale which has not yet reached the burning area. The condensed vapors yield up to 72 gallons of oil per ton of shale. When the shale oil will become a commercially competitive product is anybody's guess. When it does, Union's technologists know how to recover it, in quantities so vast that it will be centuries before the nation runs out of oil.

Oil as it comes from the sands that have trapped it for ages is seldom clean enough to be used except as a cheap fuel oil. Removing the impurities and converting them by chemical alchemy into useful by-products has become a side line so important to the oil industry that it makes necessary and justifies such expenditures as Union's new 5-million-dollar experimental laboratory at Brea. Each field presents a special problem, depending upon the extraneous ingredients picked up by the crude in the oil pool below.

Union's Santa Maria field is a striking example. Every thousand barrels of Santa Maria crude contained up to 150 pounds of salt. The $750,000 plant to get rid of this salt looked like so much expense until Union's technologists found in it sub-impurities such as silver, nickel, cobalt, iron, and vanadium. That set experimenters on the track of processes to recover these valuable minerals. If and when the researchers at Brea come up with a means of capturing the 150 tons of vanadium, a rare mineral used to make steel harder, pumped from Union's wells each year, they will have found the way to pay back into Union's treasury in six or seven years the entire 5 million dollars paid out for the laboratory. The company's chemists did find one bucket of gold at the end of the Santa Maria research rainbow. It is carbon dioxide, plentiful in gas from the wells. The carbon dioxide now becomes tons of dry ice in the first plant to extract this "cold fuel" from natural gas. Every ton of the stuff the plant can recover is contracted for in advance.

These and other experiments too numerous to recount have brought Union's scientific staff to a milestone which they call "an exciting period, technologically, with a future even more exciting." The oil hunt is no longer limited to far-flung places of the globe for new underground reserves. It is in each barrel of crude oil as it comes from the ground, a package of potential products only partially unlocked.

# CHAPTER FOURTEEN

# Big Business Is Good for Little Business

WHEN the Union Oil Company of California was organized in 1890, it was the merger of four little businesses controlled by the founders. Even after the merger, Union Oil was still a little business. It sold less than 85,000 barrels of oil that year. Most of this was fuel oil, the cheapest petroleum product on the market. Even fuel oil was so hard to sell that Lyman Stewart was obliged to devote much of his energies persuading or cajoling prospective customers to try oil in competition with coal.

By its sixtieth year Union's sales had pyramided 350-fold. The company's original four products—fuel oil, kerosene, grease, asphalt—had increased to four hundred, too numerous to mention. Instead of taking orders, Union's marketing organization was selling a service, not too different from that of a public utility, the rendering of which disposed of more than a billion gallons of petroleum products each year.

In the course of rendering this public service, Union had grown into a big business which made little business for some five thousand individuals and smaller companies. This remarkable evolution of many businesses from the successful growth of one business, which grew bigger as it shared its operations with other enterprisers, was typical of the American oil industry as a whole, an industry noted for its rugged individualism as it neared the ripe young age of a century.

Though Union was one of the first oil companies in the California field, and strong largely because its founders had staked out enviable reserves while the staking was good, three generations of Union Oilers had to fight for the markets. In the beginning they battled for business with a score of rivals, only one of whom survives. Yet in 1950, there were 1,200 producing oil companies in California alone, and 52 of them were operating refineries turning out competitive products. In spite of its size, Union was still known

243

*First truck at Los Angeles heralds beginning of the end for horse-drawn vehicles.*

as an independent and a champion of smaller independents.

Union's growth marketwise is as significant as the feats of its oil hunters, its oil pumpers, and the technologists who captured 396 new products from a barrel of oil. It was five years after the company's organization before its wells yielded enough oil, 90,000 barrels a year, to justify opening sales offices in Los Angeles and San Francisco. Then, ironically, the output fell off to two-thirds, discouraging further market expansion until 1904, when the company bought the San Francisco plant of the Pacific Steam Whaling and Arctic Oil Works, which had acted as Union's agent as far north as Kotzebue on the Arctic Circle and as far south as Valparaiso, Chile.

By that time, Union had built the first units of the Oleum plant and it had 375,000 barrels of crude flowing from its wells each year. The refinery men had learned how to make better kerosene and fuel oil, an imposing list of greases and lubricants. Union's salesmen had something to sell and they went after the business. John Baker, Jr., took charge of the San Francisco office, invaded the Hawaiian Islands, ranged far afield for outlets in Latin America, the Eastern seaboard states, and Europe, selling oil as it had never been sold before by a Western company. He sold so much oil that Union was able to contract to market all the crude of the 150 San Joaquin Independent Producers, build an 8-inch Producers' Pipe Line to the sea, and build a fleet of tankers. It was at this milestone in its corporate life, 1910, that the Union Oil Company of California emerged definitely as a big business.

Yet the company had not even tapped the market that was to make it still bigger, and position it to set hundreds of other men and women and companies up in

244

*First Union Oil service station opened at Sixth and San Mateo Streets, Los Angeles, in 1913.*

business on their own. This was the modern service station, which was distinctly a Western evolution, filling the motorist's gas tank and crankcase, checking his tires and radiator, cleaning his windshield, and incidentally selling more dollars' worth of petroleum products than any other outlet the industry has so far devised.

Union's first retail outlet for gasoline and other products was opened at Sixth and Mateo Streets in Los Angeles in 1913. Compared to today's sleek service stations, it was a primitive affair, a corrugated iron roof protecting a portable hand pump, which with one slow turn of the handle pulled a gallon of gas from a drum and pushed it into the tank under the automobile's seat. The station also sold kerosene, lubricating oil, grease, and fuel oil to any customer who wanted to bring his can and have it filled.

It seems incredible that, despite the excellent sales at this pioneer customer out-

let, the service station should have been so slow in evolving. It was not until 1917, when Union bought the Pinal-Dome Oil Company, with 20 service stations already established in Los Angeles, Oakland, Santa Ana, and Anaheim, that the company began to take the retail customer seriously. By this time, Union had established more than a hundred bulk-marketing stations in key cities of the Pacific Coast, in Hawaii, the Orient, Latin America, and Alaska.

With the former Pinal-Dome stations pushing Union products, sales soared. The marketing department opened new service stations as fast as they could be built or leased. Concluding that most of the hastily built retail outlets were unsightly blots on the landscape, the Union management held a contest in 1918 among Western architects for the design of a better looking functional station suitable for any neighborhood. Out of the hundreds of designs

245

submitted evolved the attractive modern Union Dealer's service station. By 1950, the modest chain acquired from Pinal-Dome had grown to 2,500 fullfledged Union service stations, most of them dealer owned and operated, as 2,500 additional outlets for Union products.

Since the service station era dawned, Union's marketers have overlooked nothing that would lure the motorist, whose patronage had become the company's bread and butter. An episode shortly after World War I, which sparked the Automobile Age, reveals the lengths to which the marketers go to keep the customers happy. A serious gasoline shortage hit the West in 1919 when petroleum products sales jumped one-quarter, overtaxing the capacity of both wells and refineries.

California alone had 500,000 automobiles registered in 1920 compared with 150,000 five years before. Union's sales department was forced to call off selling in the new territories it had invaded. By mid-July of 1920, Union's service stations, along with those of its competitors, were nearly dry. The Union management hurriedly bought 2 million gallons of Texas gasoline and chartered special trains of tank cars to rush the gas west at express-train speed.

"The first trainload of 26 tankers, bearing a capacity of 202,000 gallons of high-test gasoline to relieve the acute

*Union has operated about every type and style of truck since it purchased its first one in 1911. Eleven years after first truck the last horse was retired and sent to the pasture.*

shortage in Southern California, arrived in Los Angeles from Wichita, Texas, today after a record run," said the *Los Angeles Express* on July 27. "Its entry into the city was heralded by Mayor Snyder who arose early and journeyed to the outskirts of the city" to hop aboard the locomotive and ride it into the station where "cheers reminiscent of a political rally welcomed the precious liquid."

This "gasoline special" was followed by a dozen others during the next few weeks, until the gas thirst could be slaked. Ironically typical of the famine-to-feast oil industry, the Western producers were swamped with crude and products two years later, as new oil wells and refinery facilities hit their stride. Union, forced to import gasoline in 1920, was shipping it to the Atlantic Coast in 1923, and still had 15 million barrels of crude in storage. But that year, sales leaped ahead 14 million dollars to hit a new high of 73 million dollars.

In a decade, the marketing department had blanketed the Pacific Coast with customer service stations. It also had 250 bulk-sales stations, a series of outlets that would double in ten more years, with 1,160 tank trucks to feed service stations and wholesale customers. By this time the pattern of Union's unique distributing system was taking form. The company maintained its 13 strategically located termi-

*Rosecrans Motor Transport Terminal between San Pedro and Los Angeles can load four 5,000-gallon motor transports simultaneously and send them away in ten minutes*

*Oleum Refinery was opened on San Francisco Bay in 1896 with a capacity of a few hundred barrels a day. In 1950 the plant could handle 60,000 barrels a day.*

nals, the intermediate storage sites between the refineries and the markets, but it operated less than a third of the 500 bulk-distribution stations and only enough customer service stations to train sales crews and test new sales ideas. Union's policy was to set up as many independent business men and women as possible throughout the company's marketing area.

This gospel of making little business out of big business got a new impetus following the outbreak of World War II, when Union's President Reese H. Taylor reverted to steel temporarily. Summoned to Washington, he was drafted for chief of

the Iron and Steel Division of the War Production Board. This duty lasted only six months, but later in the war he was called back again to assist in establishing the Fuels and Lubricants division of the Army. When he returned to Union in 1942, Taylor had seen a new light.

"Businessmen have so much trouble in Washington primarily because the government people don't understand what makes a business function," he reported.

Taylor concluded that Union could do a job not only for itself but for business generally by devoting much of the company's advertising appropriation to telling the public how one business—Union Oil Company of California—functioned, pinning each story down to one employee and what he did, or one dealer or contractor and how each fitted into the highly productive American free-enterprise system.

It was an appropriate time to try out the idea. Gas rationing had cut down the motorist's quota to less than he wanted. It was poor fuel at best because the best from each barrel of oil went into fuel for engines of war. Service stations functioned poorly because the young men were in uniform. Caught in a similar predicament, many manufacturers tied their advertising to their roles in winning the war to keep their names before the public. Taylor didn't like to hitch Union's kite to the war effort, even though that took up most of the company's capacity.

Talking about the free-enterprise system in an institutional way encountered considerable resistance among Union's marketers, who thought advertising ought to sell products. The first full-page ad of the now famous free-enterprise series was worked up by Margaret Corrie (who became Mrs. Reese H. Taylor in 1944) who was advertising manager at the time. Published in April, 1943, it explained in six simple paragraphs and seven sketches how Union's 1942 net profit of $5,537,-329 actually meant $147.94 for each of 31,653 shareholders, with $27.52 for each stockholder left in the business.

Each month a new story, bearing always the slogan "America's Fifth Freedom Is Free Enterprise," followed, giving the public an insight into how a lot of individuals and their dollars teamed up to make a big corporation. One explained "How to Drill an Oil Well for $2.08," each stockholder's share in a new hole. Another, picturing an oil-field workman, told how "It Cost $35,000 to Get This Man a Job." "Meet Ten Capitalists" introduced the public to 10 typical Union stockholders, a stenographer, a service-station man, an engineer, a housewife, a minister, an optometrist, a barber, a well driller, an army sergeant, and a boatbuilder.

Intended only as a wartime measure, the free-enterprise series caught the public's imagination, and so many people wanted copies of the advertisements that Union had to publish them in book form. This publication, *How and Why American Business Functions,* ran through seven editions of increasing size in the next seven years. To the surprise of the marketing department, talking about the men and women who made up the Union Oil Company proved a product seller as well as an idea seller.

Expanded, the postwar series hammered away on the theme that $35,000 worth of tools made each Union Oiler a highly efficient producer; that profits meant a lot of small checks for thousands of small investors; that companies, like people, have cost-of-living problems; and they presented portraits of real capitalists. One told how Neal McGinley, who came from Ireland at the age of twenty-one, went to work as a pumper in Union's Lompoc field, raised a family of six boys and one girl, all college graduates, lost two sons in the war; though he still held a job comparable to the one with which he started in 1911, he drew three times as

249

*Arthur C. Stewart, vice-president in charge of marketing for Union Oil Co. of California.*

much take-home pay for less than half as many hours. Another told the story of the Pagenkopp brothers, who, after returning from World War I, launched themselves in Santa Ana with Union's backing in a service-station business now valued at $85,000 with a $100,000-a-year volume, and profits enough to enable each brother to own a sizeable ranch for a home and a side line.

The Pagenkopp brothers were typical of several thousand Union little business-men, who had prospered along with the

company. Some became big operators on their own, such as Earl McKale, who started with one service station in the Northwest and built up a thriving chain in Seattle, Portland, and San Francisco. Nearly all the distribution depots are the businesses of individuals put on their financial feet by the company.

But not all of them were in the marketing end. The Oleum refinery had contracted with 65 free enterprisers for services formerly performed by people on the payroll. The Wilmington refinery has 69 contractors, the transportation department deals with more than four hundred commercial truckers, the field department uses 270 contractors for drilling, construction, well pulling, and other operations. How Union contracts, plus financial backing in many cases, have helped more than three thousand men and women to establish themselves in their own businesses is a convincing demonstration that "free enterprise, America's fifth freedom," is a practical system that works.

Take Joe Robinson and his Santa Fe Drilling Company, for example. Robinson and 62 former employees of the Union Oil Company drilling department incorporated the Santa Fe Drilling Company, with Robinson as president, late in 1946. When Robinson came to Vice-president "Cy" Rubel, proposing that he and his 62 colleagues organize a million-dollar company to take over the firm's drilling equipment and put ten crews in the field making hole for the company, the Union management accepted. Robinson and associates made the business pay from the start. In three years they were out of debt, their assets had doubled, and they had 20

*Oleum Refinery's facilities are skillfully designed for maximum efficiency in unloading cargoes of crude and reloading ships, tank cars, and trucks with refined petroleum products.*

drilling crews scattered from Canada to Italy, and owned the largest independent drilling company in California.

Back in 1939, an enterprising chauffeur entered a Union service-station competition for a better paint cleaner and preserver. George Sevelle's product was better than any of the dozen others submitted. Since he had concocted the stuff primarily to wash and polish cars, Sevelle was astonished when the contest manager asked if the stuff would do to wash service stations. Out of that question grew a deal in which Sevelle agreed to wash 5 Union service stations on a regular schedule. By the end of the year, the contract had been increased to 150 stations. Then it was jumped to 1,100 stations, and finally to 4,000, which Sevelle scrubs with the aid of 35 men, 14 big trucks, and 5 house trailers in which his crews live in comfort while on the road.

George Sevelle has built station washing into a sizeable and profitable business. Born in San Jose, an honorary Boy Scout commissioner and a community leader, Sevelle styles himself "one of the oldest native sons of Negro parentage in California." His paternal grandfather came from Key West, Florida, and settling in Grass Valley became the first Negro owner of a gold mine in the state. His maternal grandfather, who hailed from Philadelphia, came West to be a chef for the Palace Hotel, San Francisco's gay bonanza inn of the luxury-loving eighties and nineties. Before his better cleaner led to his contract with Union, Sevelle had tried a lot of callings—doorboy, window dresser, pantryman, waiter, candymaker, serviceman for electric automobiles, mechanic for famous racing drivers.

"When Union asked me to wash service stations, it was all right with me, so long as I sold my product," says Sevelle. "There was one drawback. I didn't have a truck to get my equipment from station to station, and I didn't have any money. It looked like no money, no truck, no contract. That's when Union came to the rescue, setting me up in business. It sup-

*Typical Union retail marine service station is this one at Los Angeles yacht harbor.*

*Large part of fishing fleet out of Monterey Bay is fueled from Union's shoreside tanks.*

252

plied the truck, charging me $1 a year. Union treated me the way I liked to be treated and in turn I've treated my men that way. That's why I have no help turnover. I still have that first little old truck Union gave me. I've retired it from service, but I keep it polished and it sits alongside my fleet of big new trucks and trailers as a reminder that in this country the big fellow is willing to help the little fellow succeed if he wants to try it on his own."

Jack Smithers, who quit cotton farming in Texas in 1924 and learned steel fabricating with the Pacific Steel Building Company in Burbank, landed his first contract with Union early in 1945, repairing a service station. "They said that if I made good I'd get another," Smithers said. "I had $250 capital and a lot of experience. Union helped me buy my first steel and a used truck. By the end of the year, I had done repairs on half-a-dozen stations and earned about $3,000."

In 1946, Smithers hit his stride. At the suggestion of Union, he went after the

work of other oil companies, not only repairing stations but building new ones. Within four years his outfit grew from Jack Smithers himself to 25 employees. Volume pyramided from $3,000 a year to a quarter of a million. Smithers was building one-third of all Union's new stations in Southern California, Arizona, and Utah. His son will join him in the business as soon as he finishes college.

Darrell T. Stuart, who painted his first Union Oil service station in Santa Barbara in 1932, now needs 40 trucks and 140 people to keep up with his contracts to keep 3,700 stations throughout the Southwest freshly painted.

"I gave them their money's worth with no cheating or skimping," recalls Stuart. "Union liked it and gave me some more jobs around town. I got an idea this might be a business to specialize in about the time the company suggested I contract to do all their service-station painting in the county. My assets at the time were a single beat-up truck and about $600. I couldn't swing the deal without more money, but with the prospects of a contract with Union and with the company's encouragement I was able to borrow. Union, you might say, set me up in business on my own."

By the close of 1933 Stuart had two trucks and ten men. Union then extended his contract to cover three counties. Eventually he spread out over California,

Utah, Arizona, and Nevada and painted stations for several other petroleum companies as well as Union.

"Sure, it was a tough struggle," says Stuart, "but when things looked the blackest the boys at Union would give me a helping hand and a pat on the back. To me, Union epitomizes Free Enterprise in action by giving the smaller fellow a 'break.' I try to spread the gospel in turn through my employees."

Perhaps that's why, on Christmas of 1949, Stuart's employees presented him with a bronze plaque testifying that "a happy family makes for a good organization."

The experiences of Union's little business people are so numerous that they would make a lively volume of human interest by themselves. Most of them follow a pattern—an idea, an opportunity, a boost, a lot of sweat and toil and initiative, and a new business is flourishing. A few have failed, usually because they expanded too fast. Union's small businessmen have helped produce and sell most of a billion dollars' worth of petroleum products during the decade ending in 1950. Union's ten-year profit, well over 100 million dollars, was considerably less than the company's 5,000 partners in business realized from these sales.

All of which goes to prove that big business can be good for little business, and vice versa.

# CHAPTER FIFTEEN

# Prospects Unlimited

SCANNING the horizon of the future as Union forged into its seventh decade, the company's management could see prospects unlimited ahead. In the first sixty years of corporate life, Union had grown from a 1-million- to a 156-million-dollar company, on the basis of stocks owned by its shareholders. That measurement was far short of the company's true worth. Oil lands, wells, and physical assets were appraised at more than three times either the par or market value of the company's outstanding shares. Even that was a conservative picture of the company's true worth, for reserves such as the huge Colorado shale holdings, with a potential of 3 billion barrels of oil, were listed on the books at token valuations, as were the unproved reserve lands.

In six decades, Union has extended the scope of its oil hunt from the little Santa Paula-Ventura area to the entire western half of the United States and Canada. The company was doubly fortunate in that its future sources of oil were entirely inside the boundaries of the United States, free from the threat of political dictatorship, police-state confiscation, or invasion. Altogether, Union had proved reserves of 360 million barrels in California, 47 million in the Texas-Gulf fields, 17 million in the Rocky Mountain-Canadian area. If the company were liquidated tomorrow, underground reserves are enough to realize $95 for each outstanding share of common stock.

The bulk of Union's oil fields and the refineries were strategically located to serve the company's marketing area, the Pacific slope. This was not only the fastest growing section of the country but likewise a compact unit blanketed by Union pipelines, tanker service, tank-truck fleet, bulk-distribution depots, and service stations.

The five thousand Union dealers in two thousand Western communities were another of the company's assets incapable of appraisal in terms of dollars. The dealers were more than fuel and lubricant mer-

255

Reese H. Taylor, president of Union Oil Company of California.

*Stewart Tank Farm near Los Angeles has total storage capacity of 3,500,000 barrels. Three of the circular reservoirs hold 750,000 barrels each and large tank holds 134,000 barrels.*

chants; each was a neighbor and a personality in his community, a businessman in his own right, and a partner in the Union Oil system. Through these independent dealers, Union's modern manufacturing plants served the consumers millions of barrels of gasoline and lubricants and numerous accessories. Through the bulk distributors they served other markets with fuel oils for home heating and power generating, with lubricants and fuels and insecticides for agriculture, with fuels and oils for aviation, and with scores of specialized products for many industries. Union's wells, pipelines, refineries, and distribution system had become a public utility upon which millions of people depended.

*When it's too swampy for a road and water is too shallow for a boat, Union's crews in Louisiana dig canals to float equipment to site and go to work in motorboats.*

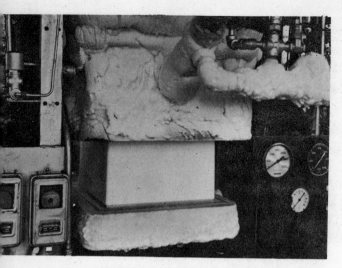

*Science now produces dry ice from Union Oil's black Santa Maria crude petroleum.*

Of all the modern miracles that meant much to Americans in their daily living, the most important was oil. Without it the country would be literally back in the horse-and-buggy days. It was a far cry from the October 17, 1890, in sleepy Santa Paula, when a handful of petroleum pioneers pooled their holdings in four struggling little oil concerns to start the equally shaky little Union Oil Company of California on its way.

Gazing into the crystal balls of the forthcoming half century, President Reese H. Taylor could see changes even more astounding than those which characterized the company's first six decades. The most revolutionary development would probably come out of the barrel of oil itself. That barrel had barely been tapped by science. It was to keep pace with this particular potential that Union invested 5 million dollars in the new laboratory at

Brea and spent another 2 million each year on research. This was the "premium on insurance taken out on the Company's future," as Vice-president W. L. Stewart, Jr., put it, and "proof that Union's management operates a going concern which we are obliged to hand over intact—and improved—to the next generation." It was also the guarantee to Union employees, dealers, and shareholders alike that their company would not fall behind the pace of the fast-moving oil industry. If the trend was for oil companies to evolve into chemical companies as well, as seemed indicated, it was assurance that ten or twenty or fifty years ahead Union would hold its enviable competitive position. For its size, this investment of Union in the future was relatively larger than that of other oil companies.

This and Union's 30-million-dollars-a-year exploration and recovery program were reassuring. In the words of President Taylor, "It has been predicted with clockwork regularity ever since oil was first put to practical use that the country would be dry of oil in five, ten, or twenty years. Our reserves and the industry's reserves are greater than ever before, and the problem is not 'will we run out of oil' but will we be able to keep up with the potential demands of the future as our civilization becomes more and more dependent upon the by-products of petroleum and petroleum gases.

"We are just scratching what we can get out of crude oil. We are in the beginning stages of the chemical unscrambling and reassembling of petroleum with the possibility of contributing tremendously to modern living. By the hypersorption process alone we can recover numerous gases at lower costs that can be converted into hundreds of new products, not merely fuels, but plastics and fabrics and hydrocarbons for the conversion and preservation of foods. The oil companies, which have been fuel and lubricant producers, will become chemical companies manufacturing innumerable products that could completely change living. Just as the oil fuel in its various forms revolutionized the living of the civilized world in the first sixty years of Union's life, so the chemical end of the business will bring about even greater revolution in living during the next six decades.

"It has been said often but aptly that oil is the lifeblood of modern civilization. Our important task is to make that lifeblood even more valuable. To do so under the American system, we must compete successfully in three fields simultaneously, for capital, for people, and for markets. We cannot fail in any of these fields and succeed in the other two. We must see that capital receives a decent wage for the risk of savings so that we can provide tools for our workers; we must see that the people working for the company enjoy the highest standard of working and living conditions possible; we can do this only by satisfying our customers that we are giving them the best possible products at the lowest possible prices. That seems like a simple and workable formula, but, human nature being as unfathomable as a barrel of oil, it will call for human as well as chemical engineering to enable the Union Oil Company to realize on its prospects unlimited."

*Union spent $2,500 for its original petroleum laboratory at Santa Paula in 1891. In contrast is this $5,000,000 modern research center built in 1950 at Brea, a few miles from Los Angeles.*

# *Appendix*

### 1883

PICO CANYON: Five dry holes; SMITH FARM: No. 1 abandoned December 31. PRODUCTION: 0.

### 1884

PICO CANYON: Star No. 1, first producing well, sold to Pacific Coast Oil Company for working capital to continue drilling; OJAI: No. 1 begun in April; ADAMS CANYON: No. 1 begun in April; SESPE CANYON: No. 1 begun in May. PRODUCTION: 2,661 barrels.

### 1885

ADAMS CANYON: Several wells drilled 300 to 3,060 feet, production from 5 to 300 barrels a day. Many dry holes. Union's "first real oil field"; TAPO CANYON: Tunneling near Piru. PRODUCTION: 4,806 barrels.

### 1886

Year of disappointment. Drilling at Ojai disrupted by water; pulled out of the field in September. Adams Canyon wells producing but not enough to meet expenses. PRODUCTION: 35,355 barrels.

### 1887

TAR CREEK: No. 1 down to 965 feet, good production; FOOT - OF - THE - HILL: No. 1 down "about a thousand feet" for good production. Both wells in Little Sespe Canyon area. PRODUCTION: 87,758 barrels.

### 1888

ADAMS CANYON: No. 16, "largest flowing well hit to date in California with initial flow of 800 to 900 barrels a day"; SALTMARSH: No. 1 located but no drilling by end of year; LOS ANGELES: Lyman Stewart and Dan McFarland drill dry wildcat near brea pits. PRODUCTION: 162,168 barrels.

### 1889

TORREY CANYON: Nos. 1 to 46 drilled this and following year; ALISO CANYON: Five wells drilled; SALTMARSH: No. 1 started; LITTLE SESPE: Kentuck No. 1 drilled to 905 feet; OJAI: Astarta No. 1 drilled. PRODUCTION: 64,049 barrels.

## 1890

TUNNELING: Near Santa Paula and Piru. Fatal explosion in "Boarding House Tunnel"; COALINGA: First test drilling undertaken in San Joaquin Valley. PRODUCTION: 84,421 barrels.

## 1891

BARDSDALE: Robertson No. 1 drilled to 1,100 feet; LABORATORY for study of petroleum authorized "at cost not to exceed $2,500." PRODUCTION: 111,-901 barrels.

## 1892

FIRST PRODUCTION OUTSIDE VENTURA COUNTY by Union Oil Company at Los Angeles; ADAMS CANYON: No. 28, "the first big well in the state," came in for 1,500 barrels a day. PRODUCTION: 139,784 barrels.

## 1893

Many Ventura County wells shut in due to opening of Los Angeles City field. PRODUCTION: 112,008 barrels.

## 1894

Wells still shut in because of heavy over-production at Los Angeles and importation of oil from Peru. PRODUCTION: 90,276 barrels.

## 1895

Wells still shut in. PRODUCTION: 77,316 barrels.

## 1896

OLEUM REFINERY opened in February; SANTA PAULA REFINERY burned in April; BREA-OLINDA: Drilling begun;

TUNNELING: New contracts let to W. J. Pinkerton for lengthening tunnels in Sulphur Mountain. PRODUCTION: 53,027 barrels.

## 1897

LOS ANGELES CITY FIELD. Wells shut in as result of concerted effort by producers to force price up to $1 a barrel. Union, Doheny, and Electric Railroad wells pumped to produce combined 400 barrels a day for local market only. PRODUCTION: 125,246 barrels.

## 1898

SIMI: Tunneling; TAPO: Contract with Hardison & Busik to dig Tapo tunnel up to 1,000 feet at $5 per foot. PRODUCTION: 215,393 barrels.

## 1899

Oil shortage. Union purchases up to 70,-000 barrels of Coalinga oil and 20,000 barrels of Los Angeles oil; ARROYO GRANDE: Began drilling 400 yards north of railroad depot. PRODUCTION: 235,297 barrels.

## 1900

FIRST GEOLOGY DEPARTMENT launched. PRODUCTION: 240,146 barrels.

## 1901

BREA: Drilling begun; BAKERSFIELD REFINERY completed. Board turned down offer of William M. Brown of Cincinnati to join in exploration in Wyoming. PRODUCTION: 273,604 barrels.

## 1902

Union acquires valuable holdings in the Coalinga, Kern River, Santa Maria, and Lompoc oil fields. In latter, where geological features indicate possibility of an American Baku, Union buys 72,000 acres of land at practically farm prices. OLEUM REFINERY increases operations to 10,000-barrels-a-day capacity. PRODUCTION: 374,736 barrels.

## 1903

COALINGA: Three wells drilled, one flowing 500 barrels a day; SANSINENA: Purchased oil rights on 3,400 acres of La Habra Rancho, known as Sansinena Tract; well went through 340 feet of good sand but was lost through series of accidents; SANTA MARIA: Leased 4,800 acres, first well produced about 200 barrels a day of 28-gravity oil "valuable for making kerosene"; LOMPOC: Two wells completed, producing 250 a day each; PURISSIMA: Union adds 43,000 acres, most in fee; properties extend for 15 miles along the sea; first well pumping 300 barrels a day; STEARNS RANCHO, TORREY CANYON, TAPO CANYON, KERN RIVER: In all these company made "valuable developments" during the year. PRODUCTION: 375,570 barrels.

## 1904

SANTA BARBARA COUNTY: Added 75,000 acres, 35,000 bought in fee under "an aggressive policy for acquiring oil lands." Drilled 14 wells averaging 2,500 feet deep in the county; HART-NELL GUSHER in Santa Maria field brought in. PRODUCTION: 747,395 barrels.

## 1905

Most of the year's drilling in Santa Barbara County, wells shut in as soon as completed due to extremely heavy overproduction in the state. PRODUCTION: 1,806,719 barrels.

## 1906

LOMPOC: Oil wells shut in "due to delay in getting delivery of three new tankers" and heavy overproduction in other fields. Union has 161,000 acres in Ventura, Los Angeles, Santa Barbara, Fresno, San Benito, Humboldt, San Luis Obispo, and Kern counties. PRODUCTION: 2,249,799 barrels.

## 1907

Drilled 36 wells this year and "proved up large areas of virgin territory in widely separated districts." Had 207 producing wells in six counties. PRODUCTION: 4,202,516 barrels.

## 1908

BREA CANYON: Put down four wells; BELL ESTATE (Santa Barbara County): Purchased 4,000 acres, drilled five test wells; PHILADELPHIA ASPHALT REFINERY authorized. PRODUCTION: 5,379,616 barrels.

## 1909

BELL ESTATE: First well flows 400 barrels a day, other wells drilled; SIMI HILLS: No. 1, a shallow and inexpensive well, is a strong producer of light oil, "an important strike"; LA BREA TRACT: 32,000 acres in fee proved up by Simi No. 1 in adjoining acreage. PRODUCTION: 4,540,785 barrels.

### 1910

MIDWAY DISTRICT—LAKE VIEW: California oil industry activity greatest in history, mostly in San Joaquin Valley. Union brings in Lake View gusher (world's greatest) on March 15; AVILA REFINERY opened. PRODUCTION: 4,704,515 barrels.

### 1911

LOST HILLS: Acquired 2,080 acres; FULLERTON DISTRICT: Two wells producing on 761 acres; FULLERTON (BREA) REFINERY built. PRODUCTION: 4,340,619 barrels.

### 1912

No new fields discovered but drilling extended. PRODUCTION: 4,477,026 barrels.

### 1913

Rotary drilling gets better results. Thirty-four new wells drilled, some exceptional producers; no important changes in land holdings, totaling 240,000 acres; NEWLOVE: First well flowing; LA HABRA: First well flowing 1,000 barrels a day. PRODUCTION: 4,838,333 barrels.

### 1914

"Every producing well ever brought in by this company is still producing oil in commercial quantities. Some of these wells were brought in as far

back as 1887." PRODUCTION: 5,005,-510 barrels.

### 1915

Drilling restricted to 22 crews, and production was down 800,000 barrels to 4,750,000 barrels. . . . Due to curtailment and "not to exhaustion of wells." PRODUCTION: 4,583,852 barrels.

### 1916

DOMINGUEZ: Company leased 1,000 acres. Union's total production to date, 75,000,000 barrels. Oil stocks in state depleted 12,000,000 barrels, so more drilling crews put to work. PRODUCTION: 5,586,795 barrels.

### 1917

MONTEBELLO: Completed two wells for 1,500 barrels daily each, drilling five more; PINAL-DOME OIL COMPANY purchased, added several thousand acres; Union acquired in fee or lease 20,000 acres. Company had 420 producing wells, production was up 11 per cent, 55 crews drilling; WYOMING: Obtained rights in 20,000 acres in state from the Sunset Oil Company; no drilling yet; LOS ANGELES REFINERY built. PRODUCTION: 7,430,154 barrels.

### 1918

"Of the company's production 60 per cent was produced from lands held in fee and 40 per cent from leaseholds." Total land holdings of both classes: 300,000 acres of which 227,000

acres were in California. PRODUC-
TION: 8,271,084 barrels.

### 1919

SANTA FE SPRINGS: Meyer No. 3 discovery well came in at 4,596 feet,
producing 100 barrels of oil carrying
"a high percentage of gasoline";
RICHFIELD: Chapman No. 1 discovery well came in at 3,168 feet on
March 11, producing 800,000 barrels
by end of year; initial production
5,000 barrels a day, discovery of
"geological importance"; TEXAS:
Leased 35,349 acres in McCullock
and Stevens counties and began test
drilling; WYOMING: Four test wells
being drilled. PRODUCTION: 8,705,-
447 barrels.

### 1920

COLORADO: Acquired mineral rights to
8,920 acres of oil shale land;
WYOMING: Drilled six wells, one
came in for 5,000,000 cubic feet of
gas daily and "some natural gasoline"; MEXICO: Company has 15,836
acres under lease and first well dry at
2,580; two big gushers produced
4,600,000 barrels and went to salt
water in December. Union has 56
strings of tools working. Total production since 1890 estimated at
110,000,000 barrels; TEXAS: First
wells drilled are dry holes. PRODUC-
TION: 8,681,308 barrels.

### 1921

SANTA FE SPRINGS: Second well on Bell
property 4,000 barrels a day; Union
has 1,350 acres leased. Company

brought in 51 new California wells
for a total of 16,000 barrels a day;
COLORADO: Bought 6,800 acres of
shale land; MEXICO: Two new dusters; WYOMING: Six wells good for
2,050 barrels in the Maverick Springs
area, 50 miles from a railroad with
no immediate outlet; TEXAS: One 50-
barrel well came in; COLOMBIA,
SOUTH AMERICA: Union purchased
425,000 acres in fee. PRODUCTION:
9,795,518 barrels.

### 1922

Sixty-nine new California wells brought in
for 27,000 barrels. Due to heavy
overproduction in California, Union
shuts down 191 fee wells, but 61
strings kept drilling to protect leases;
HUNTINGTON BEACH: Brooks No. 1
discovery well; SIGNAL HILL: Union
brought in one well for 2,000 barrels
but has very little acreage in the
area; TORRANCE: First wells come
into production; REDONDO: One
well, 100 barrels daily; WYOMING:
Thirteen wells in Maverick Springs
area, all shut in. PRODUCTION: 12,-
092,194 barrels.

### 1923

Union's production of 18,741,633 barrels
was 50 per cent greater than for
1922, and Union shut in 165 fee
wells capable of producing 35,000
barrels a day. COMPTON: Callender
No. 1 came in, 1,400 barrels daily;
DOMINGUEZ field discovered; COLO-
RADO: A 75,000,000-cubic-foot gasser near Fort Collins, blew for
twenty days. Union had 10,000 acres

under lease; WYOMING: First well in Circle Ridge Dome came in for 150 barrels a day; UTAH: Took over 2,560 acre leasehold but no drilling. PRODUCTION: 18,409,810 barrels.

## 1924

ROSECRANS: First well came in in May, by end of year Union was getting 3,100 barrels a day from field, a sleeper; Test wells drilled at DOMINGUEZ, SAUGUS, RIO BRAVO, WISECARVER; WYOMING: Drilling on two sites; COLORADO: Whitaker Well on Fort Collins structure came in for 600 barrels a day; NEW MEXICO: Test well in Vermejo Park, Bartlett Ranch, down 3,040 feet; BRITISH COLUMBIA: Purchased 3,840 in fee of potential oil land. PRODUCTION: 14,658,594 barrels.

## 1925

Union had 150 wells shut in, equal to 13,000 barrels a day. Company buying 51,000 barrels a day rather than use up its own crude. Test wells put down in Los Angeles Basin and San Joaquin Valley; WYOMING: Discovered new field at Lake Creek with 500-barrel well; UTAH: Acquired 1,400 acres but no drilling. PRODUCTION: 12,483,000 barrels.

## 1926

NORTH POSO CREEK: Proved up with two wells; STEARNS LEASE in Orange County: Four wells drilled to lower sands for 850 barrels a day each; RICHFIELD: Four wells drilled deeper came in for 550 barrels each. "Dur-

ing year considerable progress made in introduction of gas-lift method of lifting crude oil, which has resulted in increased production of both crude and natural gasoline at lower costs." WYOMING: Oil found by others on South Sunshine structure where Union held 8,700 acres under lease and permit; COLORADO: Twelve strings at work testing; NEW MEXICO: Union abandoned holdings of 121,000 acres and moved out; VENEZUELA: Took half interest in 880,000 acres for exploration. PRODUCTION: 12,774,000 barrels.

## 1927

Fifth straight year of overproduction in California. Union had 177 wells capable of producing 19,000 barrels a day shut in and was buying 75,000 barrels a day. POSO CREEK: Well Tribe No. 1 with initial production of 400 barrels daily extended field 3 miles south from discovery well; HUASNA ANTICLINE in San Luis Obispo County being test-drilled; WYOMING and COLORADO: Combined production was 1,200,000 barrels for year. PRODUCTION: 12,103,000 barrels.

## 1928

HOVEY HILLS and SAN EMIDIO RANCH in San Joaquin Valley test-drilled; HAWTHORNE and LAWNDALE, three test wells; OLD BELRIDGE KERN FIELD: Five wells completed at only 650 to 700 feet and producing 65 barrels a day each; COLORADO and WYOMING: Union sold oil holdings to Continental Oil Company, bought more shale land; VENEZUELA: First test well abandoned at 6,500 feet; MEXICO: Three dry wells on new 26,000-acre lease in Veracruz. PRODUCTION: 10,605,000 barrels.

## 1929

California production at all-time high of 292,000,000 barrels; Union had 46 crews at work, 191 wells shut in, and 82 wells curtailed. Buying 67,000 barrels a day. WASHINGTON: Four dry holes in 6,400 acres near mouth of Columbia River; HOVEY HILLS: Test well for 300 barrels a day opens new zone; SANTA FE SPRINGS: 35 wells completed; MARICOPA FLAT: Test well being drilled; POLE CANYON anticline in Salinas Valley being tested. PRODUCTION: 16,266,000 barrels.

## 1930

California production of 228,000,000 barrels down 70,000,000 barrels from 1928. Union has only ten crews at work, but spent $5,300,000 for land and leases, including $4,000,000 for undivided half interest in King lease in Kettleman Hills. NORTH DOME OF KETTLEMAN HILLS: First well reached 5,342 feet on 160 acres held jointly with Amerada Petroleum Company; NORTH BELRIDGE: First well to deeper zone; LOMPOC: Proved area substantially increased; VENICE-PLAYA DEL REY: First well on 742-acre lease completed with 880-barrel production; VENEZUELA: Second test well is failure. PRODUCTION: 13,428,000 barrels.

## 1931

Union production down 3,736,921 barrels due to state-wide curtailment program. Company had 450 wells producing 40,000 barrels a day, 507 wells shut in, but production increased to 84,000 barrels a day by end of year; six drilling crews in field. NORTH DOME: First well in Amerada King lease completed July 2 to depth of 8,310 feet for 20,000 barrels a day of 37-gravity oil. Well cut back to 4,000 barrels a day. PRODUCTION: 11,002,000 barrels.

## 1932

NORTH DOME: Second well completed November 4 at 8,500 feet for 12,000 barrels and cut back to 2,000 a day; DOMINGUEZ: Ten wells drilled to conform to lease requirements. Union had 472 wells shut in, 481 producing. PRODUCTION: 11,963,000 barrels.

## 1933

Union cut production back 1,500,000 barrels to 14,000,000 barrels to further curtailment program. NORTH DOME: Third well completed in April for 8,900 barrels at 8,600 feet and cut back. PRODUCTION: 10,891,-000 barrels.

## 1934

Union production up 5 per cent. Company has 539 wells producing 44,000 barrels a day, with 461 shut in. Drilling brought in new wells producing 50,000 barrels daily. MOUNTAIN VIEW: Kernco No. 1 completed to

267

extend producing territory 2 miles; SANTA MARIA: Morell No. 1, a straight wildcat, discovers field of heavy oil several miles north of old Santa Maria fields. PRODUCTION: 11, 677,000 barrels.

## 1935

Production up 3,800,000 barrels. Company has 686 wells producing 64,000 barrels, 403 wells shut in. Begins extensive drilling to extend proved fields, drilled 95 new wells with 81,000-barrels-a-day production. PRODUCTION: 14,512,000 barrels.

## 1936

Extensive geophysical and exploratory drilling; 83 new wells drilled, good for 34,000 barrels a day; 580 wells producing 58,000 barrels daily, 478 shut in. SANTA MARIA VALLEY: Now field of major importance, with nine producing wells from 2,500 to 4,000 feet; Union owns 3,500 acres; DOMINGUEZ: Callender No. 44 hit a deeper formation for 1,500 barrels a day; four other new wells good for 11,000 barrels a day total; SANTA FE and RICHFIELD: Deeper drilling; SAN JOAQUIN area: Seismic work in new areas. PRODUCTION: 15,673,762 barrels.

## 1937

Union's production hit all-time high of 22,961,604 barrels, most of it from wells on leaseholds with fee-land wells shut in; 75 new wells are good for 40,000 a day. SANTA MARIA VALLEY: New wells extend field 5

miles; RIO BRAVO: Discovery well good for 2,600 barrels a day; Union has 2,400 acres in area, drills world's deepest well to 11,302 feet; NEBRASKA: Company leases 30,000 acres for exploration; TEXAS: Four wells with combined flow of 1,750 barrels on Keeran lease in Southwest; NEW MEXICO: Leases 560 acres for test well; ALASKA: Leases land on Bear-Salmon creeks for testing. PRODUCTION: 17,301,416 barrels.

## 1938

Union's production down 2,000,000 barrels due to partial curtailment; company has 643 wells producing, 504 shut in, drills 68 new wells good for 49,000 barrels a day. RIO BRAVO: Six new wells with a daily potential of 30,000 barrels cut back to 2,000 under curtailment program; ROSECRANS, SANTA MARIA VALLEY, MONTEBELLO: Development work; NEBRASKA: Drilled dry hole in western part of state. PRODUCTION: 15,703,-000 barrels.

## 1939

Prospecting for deeper zones and exploring new areas, company drilled 70 wells and completed 63 for 86,500 barrels a day; had 715 wells producing and 506 shut in. NORTH COALINGA NOSE: First well completed for 3,000 barrels but cut back to 185; COLE'S LEVEE in San Joaquin: Four wells completed for 4,400 barrels, cut back to 740. Stringent voluntary curtailment in effect by

December. PRODUCTION: 14,379,000
barrels.

### 1940

LOUISIANA: Discovery well in Vermillion
Parish comes in at 10,658 feet.
PRODUCTION: 15,050,000 barrels.

### 1941

Proved crude reserves estimated at 316,-
000,000 barrels. Of 103 wells drilled,
94 were producers for potentials of
105,000 barrels a day. By end of
year Union had 1,542 producing
wells, of which 306 were shut in.
DOMINGUEZ: Earthquake damaged
several wells; VENEZUELA: Disposed
of all holdings. PRODUCTION: 15,-
494,000 barrels.

### 1942

Production in California, Louisiana,
Texas, and Wyoming increased 17
per cent during year. LOUISIANA:
Two discoveries, Vinton Field, Fresh
Water Bayou; White Lake field dis-
covered in 1940 extended. PRODUC-
TION: 18,073,000 barrels.

### 1943

Of the 101 wells drilled during the year,
82 were producers. KANSAS: Discovery well in Sheridan County, western Kansas, for 436 barrels a day at
3,800 feet; UTAH: Wildcatting;
ARIZONA: Wildcatting; TEXAS: Enter
West Texas for first time with 2,000
acres around the discovery well, and
another 60,000 under lease; first well
good for 550 barrels a day; ARKAN-

SAS: Wildcatting; LOUISIANA: Daily
production up to 4,970 barrels,
large reserves established. PRODUC-
TION: 21,719,000 barrels.

### 1944

All-time production high of 31,776,000
barrels. Gross reserves increased by
44,500,000 barrels. LOUISIANA:
Produced 2,312,000 barrels with
new field discovered at West White
Lake in Vermillion Parish; MON-
TANA: Union bought the Glacier
Production Company with 172 wells
producing 2,700 barrels a day,
estimated reserve of 20,000,000 barrels and small refinery at Cut Bank;
CALIFORNIA: Graham-Loftus properties in Orange County purchased;
PARAGUAY: Exploration rights to 55
million acres acquired, geophysical
work begun. PRODUCTION: 24,688,-
000 barrels.

### 1945

"For fourth consecutive year company's
gross crude production exceeded all
previous records." SANISNENA: Discovery well near La Habra in Los
Angeles Basin; CYMRIC AREA in San
Joaquin Valley: Limited but prolific
pool; TEXAS: Two new wells in production on Boling Dome in Wharton
County; LOUISIANA: Extensive development in Vinton and East White
Lake fields. PRODUCTION: 26,380,-
000 barrels.

### 1946

Union added 55,000,000 barrels to its
underground reserves. Several pro-

ducing wells completed in West Texas, Gulf Coast area, and Montana with 47 dry holes. WASHINGTON: 195,000 acres under lease; PARAGUAY: Exploratory work extended and first test well started; LOUISIANA: Two gas fields put into production; CANADA: Gas reserves of exceptional promise discovered. PRODUCTION: 25,517,000 barrels.

### 1947

Company pushes exploration in 13 states and Canada and Paraguay. New production in California amounted to 18,600 barrels a day. Proved crude reserves reached 507,000,000 barrels. Company drilled 310 wells and completed 217 as producers. WASHINGTON: Test well being drilled; PARAGUAY: First test well dry, second being drilled; LOUISIANA: Tigre Lagoon gas reserves increased in Vermillion Parish and Terrebonne Parish; CANADA: Gas areas extended. PRODUCTION: 27,743,000 barrels.

### 1948

New production record of 36,192,000 barrels. Drilled 291 wells, got 235 producers. Exploration pushed in 12 states, Alaska, Canada, and Paraguay, in Gulf of Mexico and under California continental shelf. LOUISIANA: Three new discoveries at Moss Lake, Lake Hatch, and Bay Junop; TEXAS: Acquired acreage in several promising fields including South Cowden, Dollar Hide, Fullerton, and Union in West Texas; production up to 122,000 barrels a month; ROCKY

MOUNTAIN REGION: Reagan field in Montana brought in for low yield at relatively low drilling costs; WYOMING: Productive well drilled on land adjacent to the Fiddler Creek discovery, company acquired interest in 475,000 acres of unproved land in Powder River basin; CANADA: Substantial gas reserves in Canada shut in pending market; NORTH DAKOTA: Seismic work begun on 2,000,000 acres; ARKANSAS: New leases acquired. PRODUCTION: 29,947,000 barrels.

### 1949

Union's proved reserves jumped to 588,000,000 barrels, largely through acquisition of the Los Nietos Company holdings (7,500 barrels daily of high-gravity oil) and Coalinga Nose and adjoining leases (6,000 barrels daily) from E. L. Doheny estate. Company drilled 210 wells, largely exploratory, for net of 147 producers. CALIFORNIA: New wells drilled in Sansinena, Sunny Hills, Cuyama fields; WYOMING: Fiddler Creek No. 1, good for 1,100 barrels daily; LOUISIANA, TEXAS, ALBERTA, CANADA: Gas and gas distillate fields extended; NORTH DAKOTA: Exploratory work on 2,000,000 acres; PARAGUAY: After fifth dry hole, exploration halted; WASHINGTON: Small production from exploratory well on Olympic Peninsula. Ground broken for $5,000,000 research center, with 12 buildings covering 22 acres for new laboratories at Brea, California. PRODUCTION: 26,032,000 barrels.

# Index

278

## ILLUSTRATIONS

Photographs in Chapter Two are from the Mather
Collection of Drake Museum, Titusville. Modern-
day pictures are by Will Connell and Rod Daley.

## Date Due

| Date Due | | | |
|---|---|---|---|
| AP1 '54 | | | |
| JAN3 '62 | | | |
| JAN 8 '62 | | | |
| JAN 30 '75 | | | |
| | | | |
| | | | |
| | | | |
| | | | |
| | | | |
| | | | |
| | | | |
| | | | |
| | | | |
| | | | |
| | | | |
| | | | |
| | | | |

WITHDRAWN

Transport Truck of Yesterday

Producer's Pipe Line starting from Bakersfiel.

AVILA

LOMPOC

PACIFIC

First tank ship

Union's First Oil Fie at Santa Paula

Southern California
THE LAND OF THE
Black Bonanza